7-16-62

3334
1526

**INTRODUCTORY
ORGANIC QUANTUM
CHEMISTRY**

INTRODUCTORY ORGANIC QUANTUM CHEMISTRY

GEORG KARAGOUNIS

Professor of Physical Chemistry
University of Freiburg, Germany

Translated and Edited by

F. C. NACHOD

Sterling-Winthrop Research Institute
Rensselaer, New York

ACADEMIC PRESS · New York and London 1962

PREFACE

Organic chemists have often shied away from the quantum-mechanical approach to their discipline. This short introduction is aimed at giving a rapid and exact survey both to the young chemist in his formative years as well as to the older, established chemist who has never been exposed to quantum mechanics.

The lack of rigorous treatment will hopefully allay the inherent fears of the timid reader and overcome any trauma he may have acquired previously. At the same time it will perhaps show him the beauty and elegance of this method of looking at organic chemistry and stimulate him into the use of more advanced books on this subject.

It was a great pleasure and satisfaction to learn that an American publishing house was interested in bringing out an English translation of my German text "Einführung in die Elektronentheorie Organischer Verbindungen."

The author is much indebted to Dr. Frederick C. Nachod for his careful translation and for many valuable suggestions. The publishers have been most cooperative in the preparation of this edition for which his gratitude is recorded.

GEORG KARAGOUNIS

Freiburg im Breisgau
December, 1961

CONTENTS

vii

CHAPTER 1

Historical Introduction.
The Quantum of Action

The manner in which great new concepts arise and gain acceptance can be likened to the germination of seeds. There are long periods of latency in darkness when hardly any change takes place. Then, after a critical measure of energy is fulfilled, there follow periods which have no relationship to the long previous time span. New facts or connections of unrelated phenomena appear which then mark a turning point in the historical development of mankind. This is followed by times of rest and perfection, until germination of new ideas produces new impulses for development. This stepwise process is found not only at the beginning of big epochs but also, to a lesser degree, in most scientific disciplines, characterized by the fact that the rhythm between change and rest is becoming more rapid in recent times. Presently we are experiencing a penetration of physical concepts which are based on quantum mechanics and which have a pronounced effect on the structure of organic chemistry. This impact serves to create order and provide means of explanation. Before we deal with it in detail we must review some physical concepts and theories.

The discovery of the universal quantum of action by Max Planck in 1900 is a turning point in the history of natural sciences. It is the discovery of the discontinuous structure of matter·which can be likened to the intuitive discovery of atoms by Democritus and Leucippus (480 and 540 B.C.), even though this explanation of existence only makes an oblique statement about the indivisible nature of energy. The property which is universally indivisible is action, viz., the product of time and energy—a concept which cannot be easily visualized. The elementary quantum $h = 6.625 \times 10^{-27}$ erg sec followed as a necessary and inescapable assumption in order to describe the laws of radiation in such a way that theory and experience would coincide.

If one had previously assumed that in any radiation process absorption or emission of energy, respectively, takes place in arbitrarily small portions—an assumption based on macroscopic experience—this concept of continuity had to be abandoned after Planck's discovery. A minimum action had to be postulated which could not be reduced further. The quantum of action cannot be partitioned and the action of any process hence must be composed of multiples of this quantity. If the frequency of a vibrational process ν is known, there result whole energy quanta $h\nu$ which are not further divisible as far as this process is concerned. The energy of a linear harmonic oscillator, for example, is expressed by $E = nh\nu$ where n takes the values of the whole integers, 0, 1, 2, 3, etc. With a known frequency ν, discrete energy quanta $h\nu$ are absorbed or emitted, but never energy values which lie between these quanta. The magnitude of energy quanta, however, is not universally constant but is proportional to the vibrational frequency ν. Hence one can find another oscillator which vibrates with a different frequency ν' and absorbs or emits energy quanta $h\nu'$ of somewhat different magnitude. For the total field of all vibrational processes there must therefore exist a continuous series of energy values. The only property which is discontinuous and equal for all processes universally is action. Numerically it is expressed by the quantum h.

This fundamental assumption resulted from the functional relationship between emitted energy $E_{\lambda T}$, the wavelength λ, and the temperature T of a black body radiator, formerly considered continuously. In the classical picture this correlation is expressed by

$$E_{\lambda T} = \frac{c}{\lambda^4} \cdot kT \tag{1}$$

(c = light velocity, k = Boltzmann's constant), where for a given wavelength λ and temperature T, the emitted energy $E_{\lambda T}$ is proportional to the temperature and inversely proportional to the fourth power of the wavelength. After the introduction of Planck's quantum theory, this relationship became much more complicated as is shown by Planck's radiation equation:

$$E_{\lambda T} = \frac{c}{\lambda^4} \cdot \frac{h\nu}{e^{h\nu/kT} - 1}. \tag{2}$$

In Eq. (1) the energy increases towards infinity for smaller and smaller wavelengths (Fig. 1, dotted curve) which is contradictory to experience. On the other hand, the curves of the Planck equation (2) go through a maximum which has a different position for different temperatures, changing towards shorter wavelengths with increasing temperature. This indeed is the behavior of the black body under the influence of heat.

The comparison and discussion of Eqs. (1) and (2) clearly points up the difference between the classical and the quantum theoretical concept of the mechanism of the radiation process. Equation (1) describes the so-called equipartition principle according to which the energy introduced into a system of oscillators is distributed among them according to its

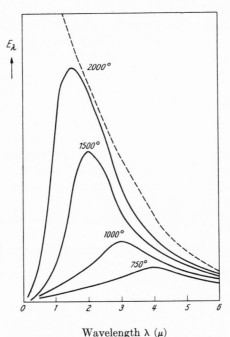

Wavelength λ (μ)

Fig. 1. Radiation of a black body.

degrees of freedom in the same manner, i.e., one calorie per degree of freedom. In contrast to this, in the quantum theoretical picture [Eq. (2)], the energy distribution among the oscillators is determined by the values of the frequency ν and thereby the values of the particular energy $h\nu$ of the oscillator. An oscillator with a higher frequency ν absorbs more energy than an oscillator with a smaller frequency since it can only absorb such energy quanta as correspond to its own $h\nu$.

If the frequency becomes very small or, conversely, the temperature becomes very large, the expression $h\nu/(e^{h\nu/kT} - 1)$ approaches kT, i.e.,

Eq. (2) becomes Eq. (1). This shows how the classical picture can be considered a limiting case of the quantum mechanical one, a fact which we shall encounter repeatedly. In our everyday experience we do not notice the quantized exchange of energy in macroscopic processes because the steps of energy exchange are very small owing to the smallness of Planck's constant h. Hence they are of no consequence because of the large supply of quanta in matter even at normal temperatures. This, however, is different when the temperature goes to very low values as we shall see in the discussion of specific heats. The same transition to the classical Eq. (1) takes place if one assumes that the elementary action quantum h converges towards zero, i.e., assumes infinitely small values. The energy exchange then is no longer provided by discrete quanta but is continuous.

CHAPTER 2

Some Applications of the Elementary Action Quantum. The Specific Heat

Inasmuch as each elementary process is determined and regulated by the action quantum there are no physical processes which are not quantized. A phenomenon which can no longer be explained by the classical continuous concept of energy exchange and which necessitates the introduction of quanta is particularly well demonstrated by the decrease of specific heat with decreasing temperature.

According to the concepts valid until 1907, the atomic specific heat at constant volume C_v for each degree of freedom was set equal to $\frac{1}{2}R$, corresponding to nearly a calorie. For a monoatomic solid body with its 6 degrees of freedom (3 for potential and 3 for kinetic energy) the atomic specific heat must be $6 \times R/2$, i.e., 6 cal/atom at all temperatures. This indeed is observed in a large number of metals at normal temperature (Dulong-Petit law). The requirement, however, that the value 6.0 should remain constant for all temperatures is not fulfilled. On the contrary, one observes a decrease of atomic heat with falling temperature which takes place at different temperatures for different solids (Fig. 2). The atomic specific heat of silver at room temperature is 5.8 cal and a marked decrease takes place only below 150°K, whereas the atomic specific heat of diamond at the same point is approximately 0.3 cal and at room temperature only reaches approximately 1.5 cal.

The explanation of this behavior was furnished by Einstein in 1907 by the application of the Planck equation to specific heats. In order to arrive at atomic specific heats in the case of an oscillator with three degrees of freedom and average energy content according to the quantum theory, one must differentiate Eq. (3) with respect to temperature

5

$$\bar{E} = \frac{3h\nu}{e^{h\nu/kT} - 1} \tag{3}$$

which yields

$$C_v \equiv \frac{\partial \bar{E}}{\partial T} = 3R \left(\frac{h\nu}{kT}\right)^2 \cdot \frac{e^{h\nu/kT}}{(e^{h\nu/kT} - 1)^2}. \tag{4}$$

Thus it becomes apparent that specific heat is a function of temperature in such a fashion that with diminishing temperature the function decreases. The magnitude of this decrease depends on the magnitude of the energy quantum $E = h\nu$, which is proportional to the frequency of the vibrating

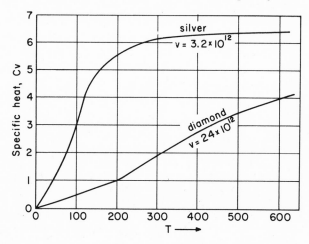

FIG. 2. Decrease of specific heats with decreasing temperature.

atoms. The carbon atoms in the diamond lattice vibrate with frequency $\nu = 24 \times 10^{12}$ whereas the atomic frequency of silver is 3.2×10^{12}. Consequently, the specific heat of diamond indicates that the quantized decrease of vibrational states takes place at a higher temperature than is found for silver. Furthermore, one can see that when T approaches infinity, the specific heat C_v approaches the classical value $3R$. Thus, both mechanisms of energy exchange—the classical and the quantum mechanical—approach each other and finally coincide.

CHAPTER 3

The Photoelectric Effect and the Dual Nature of Light

In this section we plan to explain the photoelectric effect by introducing the elementary action quantum, since it forms a transition between the necessary dualistic concept of the nature of light and hence forms a transition to the concept of corpuscles as waves.

When light falls on a metal plate, electrons are emitted (Hertz,[1] Hallwachs,[2] and Lenard[3]). Their velocity does not depend on the intensity but on the color, in other words, the frequency of the incident light. By increasing the intensity of the light one only increases the number of emitted electrons. The connection between energy and frequency cannot be explained through the wavelike propagation of the light since, as a measure of energy of the wave train, it would assume the square of the amplitude and thus would not establish a connective relationship between energy and wavelength. However, if one assumes that light consists of corpuscles, that is, a stream of fine particles, namely photons, which have an impulse of $h\nu/c$, the energy content of the photon according to the quantum concept is the product $h\nu$, and one arrives at the Einstein[4] relationship (1905)

$$\tfrac{1}{2}mv^2 + P = h\nu. \tag{5}$$

The kinetic energy of the emitted electron, $\tfrac{1}{2}mv^2$, plus the work P which it must expend in order to leave the metal surface is equal to the energy content of the photon, $h\nu$. When photons collide with the metal, they give off their total energy content to the electrons and are destroyed in the

[1] H. Hertz, *Ann. Physik* [3] **31**, 983 (1887).

[2] W. Hallwachs, *Ann. Physik* [3] **33**, 301 (1888).

[3] P. Lenard, *Wien. Ber.* **108**, 1649 (1898); *Ann. Physik* [4] **2**, 359 (1900); [4] **8**, 149 (1902); cf. J. J. Thomson, *Phil. Mag.* [5] **48**, 547 (1899).

[4] A. Einstein, *Ann. Physik* [4] **17**, 132 (1905); [4] **20**, 199 (1906).

process. Now, the above-mentioned connection between velocity of emitted electrons and the color of the incident light is established.

For each corpuscular photon which falls on the metal surface, one electron is liberated immediately. If one would like to explain the photo-electric electron emission by the incidence of a wave train, one would have to stipulate accumulation of energy in the case of low light intensity, until such a level is reached that a quantum has been accumulated. For example, in the case of x-rays, one would have to wait a century for the electron to leave the metal surface. Experience shows, however, that the electron is emitted for all wavelengths instantaneously.

The marked success of the assumption of the corpuscular nature of light in the case of the photoelectric effect has not solved the problem in general. There are, on the other hand, a group of phenomena, such as dif-fraction and interference, which can better be explained with the wave nature of light. Hence one has had to accept a compromise of corpuscular properties on the one side, and wavelike properties on the other, depending on the experimental method employed. Or, as one likes to express it nowa-days, if one draws the utmost consequence, light has no nature *per se*, but only coupled with the instrumental techniques with which it interacts; it behaves either as a corpuscle or as a wave.

CHAPTER 4

The Bohr Atomic Model.
Its Success and Shortcomings

In the atomic model of Rutherford[1a] (1911) the mass of the H atom is concentrated in a small positively charged space of 10^{-13} cm diameter and the negative electron moves around it in an orbit. The resulting centrifugal force is compensated by Coulomb attraction of the two particles. Such an atom is unstable. An accelerated charge radiates energy and hence the electron should continuously shorten its internuclear distance until it finally, after a very short period of time, falls into the nucleus. Other difficulties in the use of this model were also encountered. For example, there was no connection between the angular velocity of the radiating electron and the spectral lines of the atoms.

Bohr[1b] introduced into the atomic model of Rutherford the elementary action quantum h (1913), in postulating that the action $qd\varphi$ of the angular momentum $q = m[r \cdot v]$ of a rotating electron in a closed circular orbital must be a multiple integer of h as expressed by:

$$\int_0^{2\pi} qd\varphi = nh. \tag{6}$$

If an electron moves in such orbitals where n may be integers of 1, 2, 3, etc., it would not emit energy. Therefore radius and velocity remain constant in time. These stationary states were considered "permitted" in contrast to the in-between states which were considered "forbidden." Instability was then associated with the "forbidden" in-between states.

If one connects the equation which equates centrifugal force and Coulomb attraction between nucleus and electron

---

[1a] E. Rutherford, *Phil. Mag.* [6] **21**, 669 (1911).
[1b] N. Bohr, *Phil. Mag.* [6] **26**, (1913).

$$\frac{e^2}{r^2} = \frac{mv^2}{r} \tag{7}$$

with Eq. (6), one arrives, as a sequel of the quantization of action, at the quantization of the radii of the orbitals:

$$r_n = \frac{1}{m}\left(\frac{nh}{2\pi e}\right)^2. \tag{8}$$

Here m stands for the mass and e for the charge of the electron. The various discrete radii represent the distances of the electron from the nucleus for the various quantum numbers n. They increase with the square of these integers. The above-mentioned relationship between mechanical rotatory frequency of the electron and the frequency of the emitted light does not exist here either, since the electron is not permitted to radiate in the stationary orbital. Bohr postulated that the difference in the energies of two stationary states would be emitted or absorbed, i.e.,

$$E_{n=2} - E_{n=1} = h\nu = 2m\left(\frac{\pi \cdot e^2}{h}\right)^2 \cdot \left(\frac{1}{n_1{}^2} - \frac{1}{n_2{}^2}\right). \tag{9}$$

This equation was the greatest success of the Bohr atom model because it agreed excellently with experience. In this manner the empirical relationships of the Balmer series of the hydrogen spectrum can be written (9a), where ν is the emitted frequency,

$$\nu = R\left(\frac{1}{2^2} - \frac{1}{n^2}\right). \tag{9a}$$

They are interpreted as an electron jump from an orbital with $n = 2$ to orbitals with $n = 3, 4, 5$, etc. Analogously, the other series spectra of Lyman with a transition from $n = 1$ to $n = 2, 3, 4$, etc., and of Paschen with $n = 3$ to $n = 4, 5, 6$, etc., could be derived. The constant R, the Rydberg constant, which had been determined previously empirically, could be related to mass and charge of the electron and to the elementary action quantum. This numerical coincidence left nothing to be desired, particularly since Sommerfeld[1c] later (1916) took into consideration the relativistic mass changes of the electron in noncircular, i.e., elliptical, orbitals and the motion of the

---

[1c] Cf. A. Sommerfeld, "Atombau und Spektrallinien," 5th ed., p. 699. Vieweg, Braunschweig, 1916.

nucleus. One should note the difference between the quantum theoretical and the classical concept of the mechanism of light emission. According to the latter, the atom contains oscillators which may assume arbitrary energy states and whose mechanical frequency is emitted as light frequency. According to the quantum concept of Bohr which uses a special atom model, only certain discrete states are permitted, the energy of the emitted light being the energy difference between two such permitted states. This strong contrast is modified in a certain way by the Bohr correspondence principle to which only passing reference can be made here.[1c]

For the fundamental assumption of Bohr, that on certain closed orbitals the electron does not emit energy in spite of its acceleration, a physical justification was lacking. This was an *ad hoc* hypothesis, which was only accepted because of its success in explaining the hydrogen spectrum. Difficulties first arose in the case of the spectrum of helium. It proved impossible to calculate the ionization energy of helium based on a model fashioned after the Bohr H model. However, the value calculated with wave mechanical methods of $198,310.67$ cm^{-1} is in excellent agreement with the experimental value of $198,310.82$ cm^{-1} [2] It soon became apparent that for certain phenomena, such as the pure rotational spectrum of certain hydrogen halides, not whole numbers but half-quantum numbers had to be introduced $(1/2, 3/2, 5/2)$ if correspondence with experience was to be maintained. While the Bohr theory was successful in the calculation of the frequency of spectral lines, it ran into difficulties in the calculation of intensities of these lines. The reasons for its failure are deeper than had been first suspected, in believing that one only dealt with mathematical difficulties in a multiple-body problem. Heisenberg demonstrated in 1925 that any atomic model irrespective of its special design was a much too detailed representation of reality and that no direct or even indirect access to such models had any meaning. They were *de facto* macroscopic pictures which had been extended to atomic dimensions without justification. This then resulted in the uncertainty principle of Heisenberg, a fundamental building block in the modern concept of quantum mechanics.[3]

Heisenberg, who restricted himself to directly observable quantities such as frequencies and intensities of spectral lines, arrived at a new system of quantum mechanics which, owing to its use of matrices, became known as matrix mechanics.

[2] E. A. Hylleraas and J. Midtdal, *Phys. Rev.* **103**, 829 (1956); C. L. Pekeris, *ibid.* **112**, 1649 (1958).

[3] W. Heisenberg, *Z. Physik* **43**, 172 (1927).

Almost simultaneously, Schroedinger developed his wave mechanics in 1926 in the attempt to quantize the atoms on a basis which was more plausible, naturally and physically, than the above-discussed quantization of Bohr. The impetus for this came from a discovery of de Broglie (1924) of the dual nature of the electron, which will be discussed further.

CHAPTER 5

The Dual Nature of the Electron.
The de Broglie Wave Concept
of Matter

The concept of the nature of light has had a changing fate. Descartes (1596–1650) and Newton (1643–1727) considered light as a stream of fine corpuscles which served to explain reflection. Later, the ideas of Hooke (1635–1703) and Huygens (1627–1695) introduced the wave concept which was taken over by Fresnel (1728–1827) and extended further. Diffraction and interference phenomena could be plausibly explained by the wave theory. The contrast between geometrical and physical optics could be considered only as an apparent one.

The corpuscular nature of the photoelectric effect as explained by Einstein (1879–1955) brought back into focus the old problem as to the nature of light. It was answered by a coalition of both concepts and the assumption of a dual nature of light. If light passes through a slit or a grating, one obtains diffraction or interference, that is, the ray behaves as a wave with a certain frequency ν. However, if the light ray interacts with matter and electrons, it behaves as if it consisted of corpuscles. In the interaction of light with electrons it behaves as a stream of particles of certain energy $W = h\nu$ and momentum $p = h\nu/c$. The concept of the ambiguous behavior of light is a utilitarian adaptation of the experimental facts.

In 1924 de Broglie[1a] recognized that a wave nature had to be ascribed to the moving electron if one wanted to impart physical significance to moving mass particles as compared to the motion of light in media of varying refractive indices. These similarities had already been noted by Hamilton (1805–1865) but no deep significance was ascribed to them at that time.

[1a] L. de Broglie, Thesis, University of Paris (1924); *J. phys. radium* **7** (1926); *Ann. phys.* (10) **3**, 22 (1925).

The mechanical principle of smallest action was propounded by Maupertius (1698–1758), which states that a projectile of given total energy E which moves in a force field follows the path of least action: that is, it chooses that path at which the product of kinetic energy E_k and time t becomes a minimum:

$$\int_A^B E_k dt = \text{minimal.} \tag{10}$$

A similar behavior is shown by a light ray moving (with varying velocity) through a medium of varying refractive index. Of all available pathways, it selects that one which requires the shortest time. This principle of geometrical optics is known as Fermat's principle and is stated as:

$$\int_A^B \frac{ds}{w} = \text{minimal.} \tag{11}$$

where w signifies phase velocity. De Broglie[1b] now established the correspondence between matter and a wave process as follows: where there is an energy W, there also exists a frequency ν, and where there is a momentum mv, there is also a wave number $\bar{\nu}$. ($\bar{\nu}$ indicates the number of waves per centimeter.) From this he derived the relationship

$$\frac{\text{energy}}{\text{frequency}} = \frac{\text{momentum}}{\text{wave number}} = \text{constant.} \tag{12}$$

In equating this constant with the universal action constant h, he could write an equation for moving particles whose velocity v becomes identical with the group velocity of a wave train as follows:

$$\frac{m \cdot v}{k} = h \qquad \text{and} \qquad \lambda = \frac{h}{m \cdot v}. \tag{13}$$

This is the famous de Broglie equation which postulates a connection between velocity v of a material particle and wavelength λ of its associated vibration process. These waves were named matter waves or phase waves.

Approximately 3 years after de Broglie formulated this equation, Davisson and Germer[2] were able to experimentally demonstrate the wave nature of the electron. They interacted a stream of slow electrons with a

---

[1b] L. de Broglie, "Einführung in die Wellenmechanik." Akad. Verlagsges., Leipzig, 1929.

[2] C. J. Davisson and H. C. Germer, *Phys. Rev.* **30**, 705 (1927).

single crystal of nickel and found that the intensity of the reflected ray at certain angles was maximal and depended on the velocity of the incident electrons. The latter fact is not understandable on the basis of macroscopic reflection laws for material bodies. Later, Thomson in England and Rupp in Germany were able to obtain interference patterns of electrons after interaction with thin metal foils. Such arrays were similar to Laue diagrams of x-ray interferences. Figure 3 shows a picture of an electron

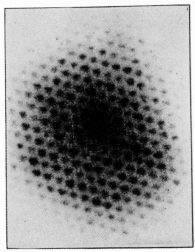

Fig. 3. Electron interference pattern of a thin mica platelet.

interference pattern on mica plates of 10^{-5} cm thickness (Kikuchi). Interference patterns could also be obtained on LiF surface lattices with beams of protons and alpha particles. Electron interferences are nowadays an indispensable and useful tool for the exploration of the structure of surfaces of solid bodies since, unlike x-rays, they do not penetrate deeply into the crystal but only interact with the surface layers of a solid lattice.

CHAPTER 6

The Wave Mechanical Representation of Mechanical Processes.
The Schroedinger Equation.
Quantum Numbers

Schroedinger's objective[1] was to find a quantization of atomic states not by introduction of postulates from the outside, but a quantization which is inherent to the atom. As an example, one may contemplate a taut string which is fixed at the two ends, and which vibrates in certain discrete frequencies (fundamental and overtones). These vibrational states are not continuous, but discontinuous and discretely following each other; they are quantized.

An electron beam of constant velocity according to de Broglie's concept corresponds to a monochromatic wave train. In it there vibrates "a certain something" which shall be designated ψ. This ψ is dependent on space as well as on time, i.e., it is a function of space coordinates and time, which is written as:

$$\Psi(x, y, z, t). \tag{14}$$

For simplicity's sake, we will consider a one-dimensional time-independent example such as a taut vibrating string. The differential equation for such a system is:

$$\frac{d^2\psi}{dx^2} = -\frac{4\pi^2}{\lambda^2}\lambda, \tag{15}$$

i.e., the distortion of ψ (in this case "distortion" is equal to the amplitude of the vibrating string) is proportional to ψ itself, the proportionality factor being $-4\pi^2/\lambda^2$. If one makes a transition from waves of a vibrating string to phase waves of moving electrons, then λ in de Broglie's equation must be replaced by

---

[1] E. Schroedinger, *Ann. Physik* [4] **79**, 361 (1926).

$$\lambda^2 = \frac{h^2}{(mv)^2} \quad \text{or} \quad \lambda^2 = \frac{h^2}{2m(E - V)} \tag{16}$$

where the kinetic energy $\frac{1}{2}mv^2$ is replaced by the difference between total energy E and potential energy V. In this way Eq. (15) becomes

$$\frac{d^2\psi}{dx^2} + \frac{8\pi^2 m}{h^2} (E - V)\psi = 0. \tag{17}$$

This is the wave mechanical equation for the one-dimensional case of a linear oscillator. If one wishes to solve this equation, that is, to determine the energy values E of the system which correspond to this wave mechanical equation, one must know the potential energy V as a function of space in the system, and substitute it into the equation. From this it follows that the Schroedinger differential equation furnishes finite, steady, and single-valued solutions only if the energy E assumes discrete, stepwise successive values. These values are called eigenvalues and the corresponding wave functions are called eigenfunctions. They represent the desired automatic quantization of the system.

The condition imposed by the differential equation is that the eigenvalues must furnish finite, steady, and single-valued solutions. One can visualize their properties by using the taut string analogy. If the string extends in both directions infinitely, i.e., is not anchored, it can vibrate with any continuously changing frequency. However, as soon as its length is fixed by clamping it at both ends, the string can only vibrate in certain wavelengths λ, which are related to its length L by

$$L = n(\lambda/2) \quad \text{where } n = 1, 2, 3 \ldots \ . \tag{18}$$

In an analogous fashion, the Schroedinger differential equation furnishes an infinite number of solutions with corresponding energy values or wave numbers $\bar{\nu}$, respectively, if no limiting conditions are imposed upon it. From this infinite number of solutions only certain solutions and energy values are selected. These permitted energy values are based on the three conditions above.*

---

* The continuous energy terms are dependent on the form of the potential curve and will not be discussed here. The reader is referred to Pauling and Wilson,[2] Kauzmann,[3] and Daudel et al.[4]

[2] L. Pauling, and E. B. Wilson, Jr., "Introduction to Quantum Mechanics," p. 64. McGraw-Hill, New York, 1935.

[3] W. Kauzmann, "Quantum Chemistry: An Introduction." Academic Press, New York, 1957.

[4] R. Daudel, R. Lefebvre, and C. Moser, "Quantum Chemistry." Interscience, New York, 1959.

We shall explain the statements above using a concrete example. The mathematically simplest vibrating system is a linear oscillator such as a diatomic molecule like H_2, O_2, N_2, etc., in which the two nuclei vibrate against each other. In the harmonic oscillator, the restoring force which brings the nuclei into the equilibrium position is proportional to the distance x of their masses, i.e., $-kx$ (Hooke's law). The potential energy V of this system therefore is equal to $\frac{1}{2}kx^2$ and the Schroedinger differential equation takes on the form:

$$\frac{d^2\psi}{dx^2} + \frac{8\pi^2 m}{h^2}(E - \tfrac{1}{2}kx^2)\psi = 0. \tag{19}$$

The solution of this differential equation leads to a ψ function for the ground state of the form:

$$\psi = e^{-ax^2} \tag{19a}$$

where

$$a = \frac{\pi}{h}\sqrt{(mk)}. \tag{20}$$

One finds that, in a way which will not be derived here, only such energy eigenvalues, i.e., acceptable solutions of the differential equation (19), are those which obey the equation

$$E_n = (n + \tfrac{1}{2})h\nu \tag{21}$$

where ν is the vibrational frequency of the oscillator and n the quantum number which assumes the integers 0, 1, 2, 3. From Eq. (21) one sees that the linear oscillator obtains a minimum energy of $\frac{1}{2}h\nu$, even for $n = 0$. This residual amount is the zero point energy, i.e., the energy which cannot be removed from a body even at the temperature of absolute zero. This constitutes a marked difference and a decisive success of the new quantum mechanics in contrast to the older quantum theory. There the quantization of energy states of the linear oscillator produced the postulate that the action of a vibrating oscillator had to be a whole multiple of the action quantum h, i.e.,

$$\int_0^{2\pi} p_x dx = nh \tag{22}$$

where for permitted energy values the following series is obtained:

$$E_n = nh\nu. \tag{23}$$

Quantization was introduced by the stipulation of Eq. (22). Equation (23), derived from it, does not provide a zero point energy since the oscillator would have an energy of zero for $n = 0$. This is in contrast with experimental experience.[5,6] On the other hand, the wave mechanical equation (19), owing to its limiting condition, automatically leads to the quantization of energy, which for $T = 0$ admits a residual amount $E_0 = \frac{1}{2}h\nu$.

The application of the Schroedinger equation to the problem of the H atom is carried out in an analogous fashion. However, the mathematical formalism is considerably more complicated. One now has a problem which is no longer linear but three-dimensional. The curvature of ψ must be taken into account in the three dimensions of space $\partial^2\psi/\partial x^2$, $\partial^2\psi/\partial y^2$, $\partial^2\psi/\partial z^2$, and for the potential energy V, the value e^2/r as a consequence of the Coulomb attraction law, e^2/r^2, must be introduced. The differential equation for the H atom thus becomes

$$\frac{\partial^2\psi}{\partial x^2} + \frac{\partial^2\psi}{\partial y^2} + \frac{\partial^2\psi}{\partial z^2} + \frac{8\pi^2 m}{h^2}\left(E + \frac{e^2}{r}\right)\psi = 0. \tag{24}$$

It is written in abbreviated form:

$$\nabla^2\psi + \frac{8\pi^2 m}{h^2}\left(E + \frac{e^2}{r}\right)\psi = 0 \tag{25}$$

where ∇^2 is the expression for the sum of the three partial differential derivatives in space and is called a Laplace operator.

We shall not give the various steps for the solution of the differential equation (25), but only sketch in a general fashion the derivation of the permitted eigenfunctions and their corresponding energy values. In so doing, we shall become acquainted with the spatial distribution of the electron cloud in the so-called s, p, d, . . . states which are extensively used in theoretical organic chemistry.

The first step for solving the above equation is a transformation into polar coordinates. The mathematical treatment is considerably simplified if one chooses a coordinate system which fits the problem. Because of the spherically symmetrical distribution of the potential V, the polar coordinate system is particularly suitable for the H atom problem. The term ψ is represented as a function of the radial distance r from the center which coincides

---

[5] K. Bennewitz, and F. Simon, Z. *Physik* **16**, 183 (1923).

[6] W. Nernst, "Die theoretischen und experimentellen Grundlagen des neuen Wärmesatzes," 2nd ed. W. Knapp, Halle (Saale), Germany, 1924; also *in* "Handbuch der Physik" (H. Geiger and K. Scheel, eds.), Vols. 9 and 10. Springer, Berlin, 1926.

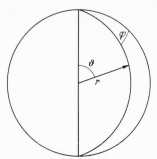

FIG. 4. Polar coordinates.

with that of the H nucleus, the azimuthal angle ϑ, and the angle φ (Fig. 4). Equation (25) then takes on the form:

$$\frac{\partial^2\psi}{\partial r^2} + \frac{2}{r}\frac{\partial\psi}{\partial r} + \frac{1}{r^2\sin\vartheta}\cdot\frac{\partial}{\partial\vartheta}\left(\sin\vartheta\,\frac{\partial\psi}{\partial\vartheta}\right)$$
$$+ \frac{1}{r^2\sin^2\vartheta}\cdot\frac{\partial^2\psi}{\partial\varphi^2} + \frac{8\pi^2 m}{h^2}(E-V)\psi = 0. \quad (26)$$

As a second step one looks for a solution in which ψ is represented as the product of three functions, R_r, Θ_ϑ, Φ_φ:

$$\psi = R_{(r)}\cdot\Theta_{(\vartheta)}\cdot\Phi_{(\varphi)} \quad (27)$$

in which R only depends on r, Θ only on ϑ, and Φ only on φ. This is possible because Eq. (26) can be separated into the three variables, R, Θ, and φ. The solutions of these equations are:

$$R_{(r)} = e^{-ar}\cdot(2ar)^l\cdot L(2ar), \quad (28)$$

$$\Theta_{(\vartheta)} = \sqrt{\frac{2l+1}{2}\frac{(l-m)!}{(l+m)!}}\,P_l{}^m(\cos\vartheta), \quad (29)$$

$$\Phi_{(\varphi)} = \frac{1}{\sqrt{2\pi}}\,e^{im\varphi}. \quad (30)$$

Here L is a power series of $(a\cdot r)$, P a polynomial of $\cos\vartheta$, $i = \sqrt{-1}$, and $a = 2\pi/h\,\sqrt{2\mu E}$, where μ is the reduced mass of electrons and protons, and E is the total energy of the atom. The parameters n, l, and m must be either 0 or the integers 1, 2, 3, etc., if the eigenfunction should have acceptable values, that is, finite, steady, and single-valued solutions. They are identified with the quantum numbers of the Bohr atom model but with one fundamental difference, in that they were not introduced artificially, but are the result of a necessary consequence of Eqs. (28)–(30). The principal quantum number n can assume only the values 1, 2, and 3 and determines in essence the energy content of the corresponding term, as can be seen from the equation:

$$ E = - \frac{2\pi^2 \mu e^4}{n^2 h^2}, \tag{31} $$

derived for the hydrogen atom.

While n, according to quantum mechanics, is a measure of the mean distance of the electron from the nucleus, the azimuthal quantum number l determines the angular momentum of the electron around the nucleus. According to the new quantum mechanics one can talk about the orbits of an electron only if one disclaims knowledge about the precise position of the electron at a discrete point in time. The momentum takes the values of $\sqrt{l(l + 1)}(h/2\pi)$, where the azimuthal quantum number l assumes values of $n - 1, n - 2, n - 3, \ldots , 1$, and 0 for a given principal quantum number n.

The parameter m is the magnetic quantum number which for a given l can be represented by a vector arrow indicating the direction of the magnetic field. Since this projection can only assume whole multiple values of $h/2\pi$, the angular momentum vector assumes a discrete angle with the direction of the magnetic field. More precisely, this vector has a precession movement. It goes through a precession motion with respect to the direction of the magnetic field in angles which discretely follow each other. It thus appears as if the space were quantized. As can be seen from Fig. 5, the magnetic quantum number m can go through all values between $+l$, 0, and $-l$, where the negative numbers correspond to the opposite direction of the angular momentum vector in the external field. The magnetic quantum number m_1 for a given value of l maintains its definition even after the removal of the magnetic field. With respect to bonding, this is of no consequence for the electron because the described states become energetically identical. In such a case one talks of degeneracy of these states, which can be removed by an external field.

The state of an electron in an atomic structure is not, as yet, clearly defined by the three quantum numbers n, l, and m. One could assume an electron to rotate in a left-handed or in a right-handed sense around its axis. This spin of the electron had to be introduced in order to explain the fine structure of atoms (Uhlenbeck and Gousdmit[7]). The momentum caused by the electron spin is given by $\sqrt{s(s+1)}h/2\pi$, whereby s can assume the values of $+\frac{1}{2}$ and $-\frac{1}{2}$. The coupling of the spin and the momentum lead to a new splitting of energy states, and thereby to the above-mentioned fine structure of the spectra. The state of the electron is now uniquely defined by four quantum numbers.

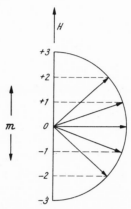

FIG. 5. Directional magnetic quantization.

In order to have a clear understanding of the spatial distribution of the ψ function, one must consider the physical interpretation of ψ. ψ itself can have no visual significance. One interprets $\psi^2 dv$ as the probability of finding an electron or a particle in the volume element dv.[8] In using this explanation one surrenders the strong causal relationship of the variables in a system of atomic dimensions. In lieu of definite statements about the magnitude of the variables in the atomic microcosm, only statements with respect to probability are made. This in turn leads to the Heisenberg uncertainty principle.

Although the explanation of the quantum theory, which is also called the Copenhagen interpretation (Bohr, Kramers, Heisenberg, Slater), was used widely by some physicists, it was not universally recognized. A group of investigators (Einstein, von Laue, Schroedinger) were not pleased by this break with the classical concept of objective reality. In the atomic dimensions, according to this interpretation, the contour of an objective

---

[7] G. E. Uhlenbeck, and S. Goudsmit, *Physica* **5**, 266 (1925); *Nature* **117**, 264 (1926).

[8] M. Born, *Z. Physik* **37**, 863 (1926); **38**, 803 (1926).

real world dissolves and is replaced by the concepts of potentiality, possibility, and probability. The initial desire of these investigators—to extrapolate macroscopic observables to atomic dimensions—can apparently not be carried out in a general physical fashion.[9]

---

[9] W. Heisenberg, *Physik. Bl.* **12**(**7**), 289 (1956).

CHAPTER 7

The Uncertainty Relationship
of Heisenberg

The attempts of the old quantum theory to translate the laws of macroscopic mechanics as we know them from daily experience to atomic dimensions is based on the tacit assumption that processes in the macrocosm can be determined with absolute certainty. It states that we can approach a body which is defined *per se* with any degree of accuracy as long as the accuracy of the measuring instrument permits it. One was, in general, quite convinced that the imperfection of instrumentation set a certain limit to this desire but one believed that any process per se could be determined with any degree of accuracy. A more thorough consideration, however, shows that this assumption is outside of experimental proof. The hypothetical experiment to define the state of a system down to atomic dimensions has led Heisenberg to the surprising result that it is impossible to characterize two interrelated (so-called conjugated) variables with any degree of accuracy. If one succeeds in determining one variable accurately, then this is done at the expense of sharpness in the determination of the second, conjugated, variable. The functional inescapable relationship of the two is such that the product of one error encountered in the determination of one variable Δq, and the other error, of the second, Δp, is larger or at best equal to the action quantum h, i.e.,

$$\Delta q \cdot \Delta p \geq h. \qquad (32)$$

The reason for this, at first, strange statement lies in the fact that one cannot carry out any measurements without disturbing the body to be measured by applying the yardstick. If, for example, one would want to determine the distance of two bodies with respect to each other, one would have to apply a measuring tape and touch them; that is, displace them ever so slightly. For macroscopic objects this displacement is without consequence.

24

For atoms, however, such changes are of the order of magnitude of atomic dimensions and hence must be taken into account. Thus, all knowledge obtainable about the state of the system tends to become obscure.

One must admit that this has nothing to do, in principle, with technical inadequacy of our instrumentation. Even with ideally constructed instruments, the above-mentioned changes of the system to be measured must still remain. These well-conceived experiments in reasoning are the great contribution of Heisenberg.

Let us assume that one wishes to determine, simultaneously, the position and velocity of an electron in the Bohr atomic model with the object of constructing the path of the electron. In order to determine the position of the electron at a certain time there is no alternative but to let it interact with a photon which is reflected by the electron, and on its return denotes its position.[1] If one repeated this experiment at various time intervals one could construct, in principle, from the sum total of all data, the path of the electron. However, in order to see the electron one would have to use a microscope with tremendous resolving power. (Resolving power is the ability to distinguish two neighboring points.) It is known that the resolving power of a microscope is given by the relationship

$$\Delta x = \frac{\lambda}{n \sin a}, \tag{33}$$

where λ is the wavelength of the photon, n is the index of refraction of the medium, and a is the angle of aperture of the microscope. If one chooses to make Δx as small as possible in order to determine the position of the electron with utmost accuracy, one would have to use short wavelength energy such as a γ-ray. The selection of short wave light, however, cannot be driven too far without influencing the velocity of the observed electron. Light, it must be remembered, is not only a wave but also a corpuscle with momentum $h\nu/c$. This momentum in the scattering of the photon on the electron is in part transferred to the latter (Compton effect). The change in momentum is

$$\Delta p = \frac{h\nu}{c} (1 - \cos \vartheta), \tag{34}$$

where ϑ is the scattering angle and Δp simultaneously is the unavoidable error in the momentum determination of the electron. The product of the

---

[1] The optical and Compton effect limitations are very lucidly treated by W. Kauzmann, "Quantum Chemistry: An Introduction," p. 235. Academic Press, New York, 1957.

error in the simultaneous determination of both conjugated variables, i.e., position and velocity (according to Bohr termed complementary parameters) thus is:

$$\Delta x \cdot \Delta p = \frac{h\nu}{c}\,(1 - \cos\varphi) \cdot \frac{\lambda}{\sin a} = h. \tag{35}$$

Consequently, we cannot determine one parameter exactly without simultaneously seeing the complementary parameter inaccurately. No matter what experiments we wish to design, the action quantum h connects the coordinates to a natural lower limit below which any statement loses its meaning. The question about actions which are smaller than h also becomes meaningless since such states could not be distinguished. It is shown that it is impossible to circumvent the uncertainty relationship since any "yardstick" of material kind (and we know no others in any physical experiments) can be used without disturbing the object to be measured.

The more sensitive an apparatus is designed, the more one approaches these changes in definition. An instructive example is the saturation phenomenon in nuclear magnetic resonance. As will be shown in Chapter 22, the absorption of electromagnetic radiation by nuclear resonance is caused by the differences in population of various energy levels. These very small differences are leveled in the absorption process so that the absorption intensity with strong radiation can be reduced to zero. This self-quenching of saturation was the reason that for many years nuclear resonance of solid bodies could not be demonstrated.

This then is a completely new situation which has had far-reaching consequences in the natural sciences and the discovery of nature itself. A number of corollaries have been drawn based on Heisenberg's principle, and indeterminacy of other processes pertaining to small dimensions was invoked. According to this, no rigorous law existed any longer but only conditioned, largely varying, degrees of probability. A causal behavior of bodies in the macrocosm is only a pretense caused by statistical multiplicity or by repetition of individual indeterminate microprocesses. The physical or apparent absolute laws in the macroscopic realm of daily experience accordingly are separated, so to speak, from the statistical process. They appear protected from the indeterminacy of the processes in the microcosm by statistical concerted action of a large number of single events. Under certain instances some indeterminate microprocesses may enter into the macroscopic field such as in biological processes which possess a steering mechanism, and thereby may impart a character of change. These extremely interesting connections cannot be discussed here in detail and the reader is referred to the papers of Jordan.[2]

One might object that the proof caused by the hypothetical experiments of Heisenberg deals with the measurements carried out on systems and not with the state of the systems *per se*. Perhaps this state could be sharply defined. Such a critique brings up the question which is philosophical rather than physical, namely, whether a world can exist independently from man who probes its nature. The physicist takes the position that a world outside of his immediate measurements lies also outside of his experience. He establishes an inseparable connection between object and subject.

The knowledge obtained from the Heisenberg principle can be best characterized by the statement made by some biologists which brings into focus the desire to employ the mildest possible method for the exploration of highly susceptible biological systems: "If one does not wish to change the cell one must leave it alone. Then, however, one does not learn anything from it."

The chemist does not need to become involved with these fascinating but puzzling questions. It is important for him that a new viewpoint was proposed which led to practical results with respect to the problems under study. The uncertainty relationship of Heisenberg has the character of a limiting principle, which clearly delineates the limits of our own power of perception. It hence makes no physical sense to attempt greater accuracy for the product of two complementary parameters than corresponds to the elementary action quantum. This new principle may be compared with the laws of thermodynamics which in their original cast were postulated as limiting principles. One may recall that it is not possible to construct a perpetual motion machine, of the first or second kind, and that it is not possible to cool a body to absolute zero. Just as in thermodynamics, the acceptance of these statements and their application has proven extremely fruitful. A number of experiences can be explained which hitherto were not explainable. Among these the clarification of predissociation spectra,[3] the justification for the existence of zero point energy, and many others are taking an important place.

---

[2] P. Jordan, "Das Bild der modernen Physik," 2nd ed., p. 61. Stromverlag, Hamburg, 1948.

[3] V. Henri, *Compt. rend. acad. sci.* **179,** 1156 (1924); *Trans. Faraday Soc.* **25,** 765 (1929); G. Herzberg, *Z. Physik* **61,** 604 (1930).

CHAPTER 8

The Spatial Distribution of Electronic Charge in Different Atomic States

The wave function ψ is generally a function of space and time and can even assume negative values in certain positions, or at certain time intervals. For this reason, not ψ itself but χ^2 is set equal to the intensity of the material wave train, since the intensity of a wave process is proportional to the square of the amplitude. On the other hand, from a corpuscular viewpoint, the density of matter is equal to the number of particles per cubic centimeter, and hence ψ^2 must be equated to the number of particles per cubic centimeter.* It can best be seen that ψ^2 has the significance of a probability, i.e., the probable density distribution of matter when one extrapolates to the transition from many particles to a single one. Its "intensity" at a specific point is apparently the probability to encounter the particle at that particular location, since we cannot make an exact statement as to where the particle will be found. This is a necessary sequel to what was said in the previous chapter about the indeterminacy of individual elementary processes and the impossibility to predict space coordinates exactly.

We shall now discuss the spatial distribution of electronic charge in the different atomic states. It is of great importance in the bonding of atoms to form a single molecule.

The differential equation for the hydrogen atom which only involves a function of the distance r is obtained from Eq. (26) by canceling out all terms which depend on ϑ and φ. If one introduces the value of the potential energy $-e^2/r$, one obtains the equation in the form:

---

* In the general case of complex functions, the probability of encountering a particle in a certain volume element dv is given by $\psi^*\psi dv$, where ψ^* is the complex conjugate.

$$\frac{\partial^2 \psi}{\partial r^2} + \frac{2}{r} \frac{\partial \psi}{\partial r} + \frac{8\pi^2 m}{h} \left(E + \frac{e^2}{r} \right) \psi = 0. \tag{35a}$$

The simplest solution of this differential equation is

$$\psi_{(r)} = e^{-ar}. \tag{35b}$$

The constant a can be obtained by forming the first and second derivatives of Eq. (35b) followed by substitution in Eq. (35a). This leads to

$$a = \frac{4\pi^2 m l^2}{h^2}. \tag{35c}$$

Furthermore, one finds the expression for the energy:

$$E = -\frac{2\pi^2 m l^4}{h^2} \cdot \frac{1}{n^2}. \tag{35d}$$

A parameter n appears which may assume the values of 1, 2, 3, and 4, if ψ shall have acceptable solutions. This result is identical with that of the older Bohr atomic theory, with the exception that the main quantum number n automatically appears. It determines the energy content of the state. The larger n, the larger the energy of the corresponding atomic state, and the lesser the binding of the electrons to the nucleus, since its distance has been increased. In order to determine the spatial distribution of electronic charge as a function of nuclear distance, one has to determine the value for the expression $\psi^2 dv$ for each volume element. All solutions of ψ which depend only on nuclear distance r and not on angles ϑ and φ are necessarily spherically symmetrical. The probability of encountering the electron in a volume element which is a distance r away from the nucleus is given in polar coordinates by the term $\psi^2 4\pi r^2 dr$. Figure 6 shows the result of such calculations in a graphical representation. One notes from these curves that for the ground state $n = 1$, a probability of finding the electron is a maximum at the distance $r = 0.529$ A which is almost identical with the Bohr model atomic radius. In contrast to the Bohr model, however, the quantum mechanical representation has the advantage that the H atom appears as a sphere in the ground state, because of the spherically symmetrical charge distribution of the electron cloud. In the original Bohr model, the H atom appears as a shallow disk. This disk would have to be paramagnetic which is not in keeping with experience.

For $n = 2$, the probability curve has two maxima which are separated by a node. This corresponds to a node plane in the function. The charge

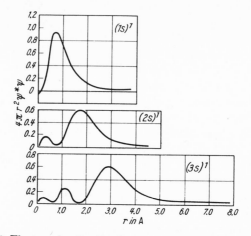

FIG. 6. Electron density distribution in the 1s, 2s, and 3s states.

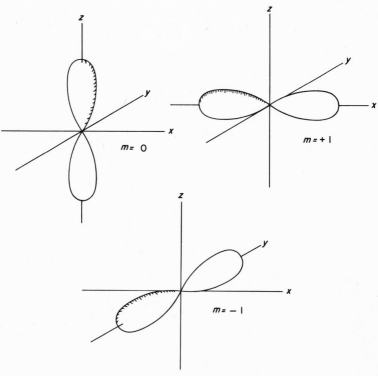

FIG. 7

distribution has the form of two concentric spheres. In analogy for $n = 3$, one finds three maxima and three positions of zero. Quite generally the number of nodal planes of ψ functions which do not depend on the variables ϑ and φ equals $n - 1$. All these states are characterized by the azimuthal quantum number $l = 0$, and are termed s states, a designation which is taken from the classification of the spectra according to theory. They form a term series, the lines of which are sharp ($s = $ sharp) (Fig. 7). If the azimuthal quantum number l, which determines the angular momentum

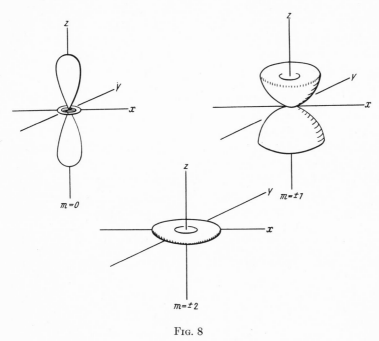

FIG. 8

of the electron, is different from 0, there result atomic states where the charge distribution has characteristic directions in space. In calculating the distribution of the charge cloud for $l = 1$, one must take into account, aside from the radial function $R(r)$, also the aximuthal function $\Theta(\vartheta)$ in forming the product $R^* \cdot R_r \cdot \Theta^* \cdot \Theta_\vartheta$ as a function of spatial coordinates. The over-all function here is independent of the angle φ since the factor $\varphi^* \varphi$ is constant. This in turn makes it necessary that the electron distribution of all states compatible with $l = 1$ is symmetrical around a Z axis. Correspondingly for $l = 1$, there exist magnetic quantum numbers $m = 0$,

$m = +1$, $m = -1$, or three states with the main quantum number 2 and the azimuthal quantum number 1 of equal energy content. This state is triply degenerate, which is only apparent if an external electrical or magnetic field is applied and hence causes small changes in the energy state (removal of degeneracy, Zeeman effect). All states with $l = 1$ are called p states since in the atomic spectra they form the so-called main series (p = principal). Figure 7 shows the charge distribution for the $2p$ state with $n = 1$ and $m = \pm 1$. It has the form of three mutually perpendicular dumbbells with a nodal point at the origin of the coordinates. With increasing main quantum number n and azimuthal quantum l, the distributions of the charge cloud become quite complicated. For $l = 2$, there exist $2l + 1$ or five states into which the energy term is split, corresponding to the magnetic quantum numbers $n = \pm 1$, ± 2, and $m = \pm 2$ and 0. Figure 8 shows the type of spatial distribution charge of the d states (d = diffuse) so-called for their spectral series with more or less diffuse lines.

All these representations of course are related to the distribution of charge of a single electron.[1]

---

[1] The representations are taken from W. Hume-Rothery, "Atomic Theory for Students of Metallurgy," 3rd ed. Inst. of Metals, London, 1960.

CHAPTER 9

The Covalent Bond.
The H_2 Molecule

The most important problem in the theory of chemical bonds is the formation of a molecule as stable as hydrogen (dissociation energy of 4.5 ev). Based on classical concepts it could not be understood why two like neutral atoms, which have no polarity with respect to each other, could be united. Also unexplainable was the phenomenon of saturation, i.e., the fact that after a certain number of ligands are bound to the atom depending on valence, no further atoms can be accommodated. The Lewis theory furnished a formal principle by proving that in the formation of a covalent bond, two electrons unite to form an electron pair. This is shared by both ligands leading to the creation of a certain order in the systematic arrangement of organic compounds. However, from a purely physical viewpoint it still was enigmatic how this electron pair produced attraction of two like atoms. Furthermore, the formalistic manner of writing this bond did not give any information as to its strength. With this summerical notation there is no room for gradations of bond strength so that all covalently bound atoms such as H_2, Cl_2, Br_2, I_2, etc., should have the same dissociation energy.

The explanation of homopolar or covalent bonds has only been furnished by quantum mechanics[1] by the introduction of a new stabilizing principle, the so-called exchange or resonance degeneracy, for which there was no analog in classical physics.

In order to describe it one represents two H atoms, a and b, by two wave functions, $\psi_a(1)$ and $\psi_b(2)$, whereby (1) denotes the electron belonging to a and (2) the electron belonging to b. They both approach each other from infinity until they reach a distance r. When the charge clouds

---

[1] W. Heitler and F. London, Z. Physik **44**, 455 (1927).

of both electrons are almost touching, but yet do not exert any force on each other, the system of the two atoms is represented by the wave function

$$\Psi = \psi_a(1) \cdot \psi_b(2).$$

It is the product of the individual H atom ψ functions. If, however, the distance r becomes so small that the electron clouds of (1) and (2) overlap, then electron (2) may also be considered to pertain to nucleus a and conversely electron (1) to nucleus b. In normal parlance, one could then say that both electrons have exchanged their position, a statement which owing to their lack of distinction escapes any possible proof. The mathematical sequel is that there must be a second wave function $\psi_a(2) \cdot \psi_b(1)$ which also describes the system and leads to identically the same energy values as the functions $\psi_a(1) \cdot \psi_b(2)$. The system therefore is doubly degenerate and one may term the described process as exchange degeneracy.

The total system of H atoms approaching each other is described by solutions which are symmetrical and antisymmetrical linear combinations of the two above-described functions, as shown in Eqs. (36) and (37):

$$\psi_+ = \psi_a(1)\psi_b(2) + \psi_a(2)\psi_b(1), \tag{36}$$

$$\psi_- = \psi_a(1)\psi_b(2) - \psi_a(2)\psi_b(1). \tag{37}$$

If the designation of electrons (1) and (2) are changed with respect to each other, the functions are not changed, save for a change in sign in Eq. (37). Hence, these linear combinations describe among others the fact that the two electrons are not distinguishable from each other.

It can be shown (cf. Pauli principle) that ψ^+ is symmetrical with respect to the coordinates when both electron spins are antiparallel with respect to each other; ψ^- is antisymmetrical* with respect to the coordinates when the electrons have paired spins. Solutions of Eqs. (36) and (37) lead to energy values of the system disturbed by electronic interaction:

$$E_{+(R)} = \frac{C + A}{1 + S} \qquad \downarrow \uparrow \tag{38}$$

$$E_{-(R)} = \frac{C - A}{1 - S} \qquad \uparrow \uparrow. \tag{39}$$

Here C stands for the Coulomb, A for the exchange, and S for the overlap integral, the importance of which will be discussed later. As soon as both

---

* A function is termed symmetrical if in changing the sign of the coordinates, the sign of the function remains; it is termed antisymmetrical when the function changes its sign in this operation.

atoms begin to interact, the two ψ^+ and ψ^- functions furnish different energy values. Equation (38), if energy E is evaluated as a function of distance r, furnishes a minimum at a certain negative energy value, whereas Eq. (39) remains monotonous at positive energy values. This means that the first solution (38) with the antiparallel spin leads to a stable equilibrium of the two H atoms, i.e., to an H_2 molecule, whereas Eq. (39) describes the repulsion at all distances r so that no molecular bond is formed. The question as to how these differences arise can be answered by discussing the integrals C, A, and S in the above equations. It can be shown that the difference is not due to the attraction of the two antiparallel, or repulsion of two paired electron spins as a direct energetic cause. Rather, the action of electron spin is important in an indirect fashion, namely, in determining the symmetry properties of the total functions, and therefore leads to solutions for the energy values. The energetic differences result from the different connection of the three integrals, C, A, and S in Eqs. (38) and (39). Of these, C and S have a simple plausible explanation. C is the Coulomb integral which describes the repulsive and attractive action of charge density of the two electrons $\psi_a^2(1)$ and $\psi_b^2(2)$ with respect to each other and with respect to the nuclei according to the potential term V:[*]

$$C = \int V\psi_a^2(1) \cdot \psi_b^2(2)d\tau_1 \cdot d\tau_2. \qquad (40)$$

The integral S is called the overlap integral because, according to Eq. (41),

$$S = \int \psi_a^2(1) \cdot \psi_b^2(2)d\tau_1 \cdot d\tau_2, \qquad (41)$$

it denotes the spatial overlap of the two electron clouds. It depends on the distance r of the two H atoms and can assume values of 0 for $r = \infty$ and 1 for $r = 0$. It is, however, more difficult to obtain a plausible idea of integral A. It is represented by

$$A = \int V\psi_a(1)\psi_b(2) \cdot \psi_a(2)\psi_b(1)d\tau_1 \cdot d\tau_2 \qquad (42)$$

and it comes about that, because both electrons cannot be distinguished, functions $\psi_a(1)$ and $\psi_b(2)$ as well as the exchanged electrons $\psi_a(2)$ and $\psi_b(1)$ have to be accounted for. The exchange integral A is particularly important in contributing towards the formation of a stable bond.

A graphical explanation is shown in Fig. 9. It gives an evaluation of

---

[*] The limits of the space integral are $+\infty$ and $-\infty$, or 0 to ∞, respectively, which are not generally written.

Eqs. (38) and (39) and shows the energy of the system of the two H atoms as a function of distance of both nuclei. We note that the E curve with parallel spin (triplet state) for all r values remains positive, i.e., the H atoms repel each other, whereas the E^+ solution with antiparallel spin (singlet state) goes through a minimum at a certain distance which approximates the Bohr atomic radius. The first state is a triplet[2] because according to the three possible orientations of two parallel spins in space it is triply

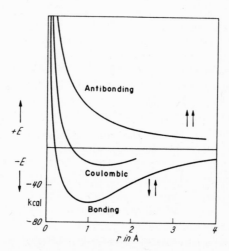

FIG. 9. Energy curves of the H_2 molecule.

degenerate. The three orientations must each have the same energy content. If the equilibrium is disturbed through a magnetic field this degeneracy is removed and the state is split into three terms. The triplet state, owing to the permanent magnetic moment of two parallel spins, is paramagnetic. The lower curve corresponds to a stable singlet state which, owing to the compensation of the spin, has no magnetic moment and is not split in a magnetic field. The reason for the stabilization of the singlet state is due mainly, as discussed above, to the quantum mechanical phenomenon of exchange degeneracy which produces an increase in electron density in the area between the two nuclei.

---

[2] Even though this is an antibonding state, it has a physical significance; see J. H. Van Vleck, *Revs. Modern Phys.* **7**, 191 (1935).

CHAPTER 10

The Pauli Exclusion Principle

The investigations of Pauli have shown that states where two or more electrons correspond in all four quantum numbers do not exist. They are unstable or "forbidden" states.

The Pauli postulate has emerged from the observation of spectra and their corresponding energy terms. It is a most important building principle which has furnished the key to the understanding of a large series of hitherto unexplainable facts. In applying the Pauli principle we realize why the rare gas helium is unable to form a diatomic molecule He_2. If two He atoms approach each other so that their wave functions interact, there results, just as in the case of the two H atoms, a splitting of states into a bonding and a nonbonding state. However, according to the Pauli principle each state can only accommodate two electrons with antiparallel spin, so

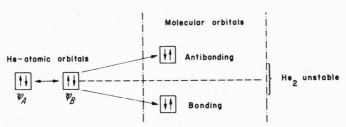

FIG. 10. Demonstration of instability of a fictitious He_2 molecule.

that the four electrons of the two He atoms must be distributed in such a manner that two are in the lower bonding state whereas two are accommodated in the upper antibonding state. Unlike the case of the H_2 molecule, here attraction would be equal to repulsion contributions and no He_2 molecule could result. Without the Pauli postulate, however, all four electrons could have been accommodated in the lower bonding state and hence would have resulted in the construction of a stable He molecule which, as we know, does not exist.

The Pauli principle had its greatest triumph in the explanation of the regularities of the periodic system. It is known that the periods successively contain 2, 8, 18, and 32 elements. The varying length of this mystic number series is explained by the double squares of the numbers 1, 2, and 3, from which the number of the elements of the individual periods then are given by $2 \times 1^2 = 2$, $2 \times 2^2 = 8$, $2 \times 3^2 = 18$, $2 \times 4^2 = 32$. For this regularity there was no explanation. If one starts with the Pauli principle whereby each energy state can only be occupied by two electrons with antiparallel spin, it can be derived that the first period must contain only two elements H and He; after formation of He, whose two electrons must have the following quantum numbers,

	n	l	m	s
1. Electron	1	0	0	$+\frac{1}{2}$
2. Electron	1	0	0	$-\frac{1}{2}$

the formation of the lithium atom which brings a third electron would cause a coincidence of the quantum numbers with the main quantum number of one of the two electrons. In order to overcome this, the main quantum number then must assume the value 2. This in turn means that the new electron has to be positioned in a new electron shell whereby a new period with a strongly electropositive element—an alkali metal—is begun. The second period has the four energy states as shown in the tabulation:

	n	l	m
1st state	2	0	0
2nd state	2	1	0
3rd state	2	1	-1
4th state	2	1	$+1$

Since all these states are doubly occupied these periods conclude with eight electrons, i.e., with eight elements. The following ninth electron must have a new main quantum number with $n = 3$, in order not to duplicate in one of its four quantum numbers any of the preceding eight electrons. This is concomitant with the beginning of a new period, which again has an alkali metal in its first place. In an analogous manner the length of higher periods can be derived. The reason that with increasing number, the periods be-

TABLE 1a
Electronic Configuration of the Elements

At. no.	Element	Shell designation: Quantum numbers / Occupation of states — K $1s$	L $2s$	$2p$	M $3s$	$3p$	$3d$	N $4s$	$4p$	Spectral designation of ground state	Ionization energy[a] (ev)
1	H	1	—	—	—	—	—	—	—	$^2S_{1/2}$	13.54
2	He	2	—	—	—	—	—	—	—	$^1S_0$	24.48
3	Li	2	1	—	—	—	—	—	—	$^2S_{1/2}$	5.37
4	Be	2	2	—	—	—	—	—	—	$^1S_0$	9.48
5	B	2	2	1	—	—	—	—	—	$^2P_{1/2}$	8.4
6	C	2	2	2	—	—	—	—	—	$^3P_0$	11.24
7	N	2	2	3	—	—	—	—	—	$^4S_{3/2}$	14.48
8	O	2	2	4	—	—	—	—	—	$^3P_2$	13.56
9	F	2	2	5	—	—	—	—	—	$^2P_{3/2}$	16.9
10	Ne	2	2	6	—	—	—	—	—	$^1S_0$	21.5
11	Na	Neon-Configuration			1	—	—	—	—	$^2S_{1/2}$	5.12
12	Mg				2	—	—	—	—	$^1S_0$	7.61
13	Al				2	1	—	—	—	$^2P_{1/2}$	5.96
14	Si				2	2	—	—	—	$^3P_0$	8.19
15	P				2	3	—	—	—	$^4S_{3/2}$	
16	S				2	4	—	—	—	$^3P_2$	10.31
17	Cl				2	5	—	—	—	$^2P_{3/2}$	12.96
18	Ar				2	6	—	—	—	$^1S_0$	15.69
19	K	Argon-Configuration					—	1	—	$^2S_{1/2}$	4.32
20	Ca						—	2	—	$^1S_0$	6.09
21	Sc						1	2	—	$^2D_{3/2}$	6.57
22	Ti						2	2	—	$^3F_2$	6.80
23	V						3	2	—	$^4F_{3/2}$	6.76
24	Cr						5	1	—	$^7S_3$	6.74
25	Mn						5	2	—	$^6S_{5/2}$	7.40
26	Fe						6	2	—	$^5D_4$	7.83
27	Co						7	2	—	$^4F_{9/2}$	7.81
28	Ni						8	2	—	$^3F_4$	7.64
29	Cu	Argon-Configuration					10	1	—	$^2S_{1/2}$	7.69
30	Zn						10	2	—	$^1S_0$	9.35
31	Ga						10	2	1	$^2P_{1/2}$	5.97
32	Ge						10	2	2	$^3P_0$	7.85
33	As						10	2	3	$^4S_{3/2}$	9.4
34	Se						10	2	4	$^3P_2$	
35	Br						10	2	5	$^2P_{3/2}$	12.2
36	Kr						10	2	6	$^1S_0$	13.940

[a] The values are taken from A. E. Ruark and H. C. Urey, "Atoms, Molecules and Quanta," pp. 280–282. McGraw-Hill, New York, 1930.

TABLE 1a (*Continued*)

At. no.	Element	Shell designation Quantum numbers / Occupation of states	N			P		O	Spectral designation of ground state	Ionization energy (ev)
			$n\,l$ 4 2 / 4 d	$n\,l$ 5 3 / 4 f	$n\,l$ 5 0 / 5 s	$n\,l$ 5 1 / 5 p	$n\,l$ 5 2 / 5 d	$n\,l$ 6 0 / 6 s		
37	Rb		—	—	1	—	—	—	$^2S_{1/2}$	4.16
38	Sr		—	—	2	—	—	—	$^1S_0$	5.67
39	Y		1	—	2	—	—	—	$^2D_{3/2}$	6.5
40	Zr	Krypton-Configuration	2	—	2	—	—	—	$^3F_2$	
41	Nb		4	—	1	—	—	—	$^6D_{1/2}$	
42	Mo		5	—	1	—	—	—	$^7S_2$	7.35
43			(6)	—	1	—	—	—	($^6D_{9/2}$)	
44	Ru		7	—	1	—	—	—	$^5F_5$	7.7
45	Rh		8	—	1	—	—	—	$^4F_{9/2}$	7.7
46	Pd		10	—	—	—	—	—	$^1S_0$	8.5
47	Ag			—	1	—	—	—	$^2S_{1/2}$	7.54
48	Cd			—	2	—	—	—	$^1S_0$	8.95
49	In			—	2	1	—	—	$^2P_{1/2}$	5.76
50	Sn	Palladium-Configuration		—	2	2	—	—	$^3P_0$	7.37
51	Sb			—	2	3	—	—	$^4S_{3/2}$	8.5
52	Te			—	2	4	—	—	$^3P_2$	
53	J			—	2	5	—	—	$^2P_{3/2}$	10
54	X			—	2	6	—	—	$^1S_0$	12.078
55	Cs			—			—	1	$^2S_{1/2}$	3.88
56	Ba			—			—	2	$^1S_0$	5.19
57	La			—			1	2	$^2D_{3/2}$	
58	Ce			1			1	2	$^3H_4$	
59	Pr	Xenon-Configuration. Shells 1 s to 4 d contain 46 electrons		2	Shells 5 s to 5 p contain 8 electrons		1	2	$^4K_{11/2}$	
60	Nd			3			1	2	$^5L_6$	
61	Il			4			1	2	$^6L_{9/2}$	
62	Sa			5			1	2	$^7K_4$	
63	Eu			6			1	2	$^8H_{3/2}$	
64	Gd			7			1	2	$^9D_2$	
65	Tb			8			1	2	$^8H_{17/2}$	
66	Dy			9			1	2	$^7K_{10}$	
67	Ho			10			1	2	$^6L_{19/2}$	
68	Er			11			1	2	$^5L_{10}$	
69	Tm			12			1	2	$^4K_{17/2}$	
70	Yb			13			1	2	$^3H_6$	
71	Cp			14			1	2	$^2D_{3/2}$	

TABLE 1a (*Continued*)

At. no.	Element	Shell designation / Quantum numbers / Occupation of states	5 d	5 f	6 s	6 p	6 d	7 s	Spectral designation of ground state	Ionization energy (ev)
			O		**P**		**Q**			
			n l 5 2	n l 5 3	n l 6 0	n l 6 1	n l 6 2	n l 7 0		
72	Hf		2	—	2	—	—	—	$^3F_2$	
73	Ta		3	—	2	—	—	—	$^4F_{3/2}$	
74	W	Shells 1 s to	4	—	2	—	—	—	$^5D_0$	
75	Re	5 p contain	5	—	2	—	—	—	$^6S_{5/2}$	
		68 electrons	6	—	1	—	—	—	$^6D_{9/2}$	
76	Os		6	—	2	—	—	—	$^5D_4$	
			7	—	1	—	—	—	$^5F_5$	
77	Ir		7	—	2	—	—	—	$^4F_{9/2}$	
			8	—	1	—	—	—	$^4F_{9/2}$	
78	Pt		9	—	1	—	—	—	$^3D_3$	
79	Au		—		1	—	—	—	$^2S_{1/2}$	8.0
80	Hg	Shells 1 s to 5 d	—		2	—	—	—	$^1S_0$	9.20
81	Tl	contain 78	—		2	1	—	—	$^2P_{1/2}$	10.39
82	Pb	electrons	—		2	2	—	—	$^3P_0$	6.08
83	Bi		—		2	3	—	—	$^4S_{3/2}$	7.39
84	Po		—		2	4	—	—	$^3P_2$	
85			—		2	5	—	—	$^2P_{3/2}$	
86	Rn		—		2	6	—	—	$^1S_0$	
87			—	—	Shells 6 s		—	1	$^2S_{1/2}$	
88	Ra		—	—	to 6 p		—	2	$^1S_0$	
89	Ac	Radon-Configu-	—	—	contain		1	2	$^2D_{3/2}$	
90	Th	ration. Shells	—	1	8 elec-		1	2	$^3H_4$	
		1 s to 5 d con-	—	—	trons		2	2	$^3F_2$	
91	Pa	tain 78 elec-	—	2			1	2	$^4K_{11/2}$	
		trons	—	—			3	2	$^4F_{3/2}$	
92	U		—	3			1	2	$^5L_6$	
			—	—			4	2	$^5D_0$	

come longer, is found in the increase of the possible energy states with larger values of the main quantum number n.

The periodic system of the elements (Table 1a) is a demonstration of the presence of an antagonism of the energetic principle, on the one hand, according to which incorporation of a new electron in the series of elements tends to seek the lowest possible energy level, and the Pauli principle, on the other, according to which the electron must search for a higher energy level, in order not to coincide in all four quantum numbers with an already existing electron. Without the Pauli exclusion principle the system of the elements would show no periodicity properties, but would change monotonously with increasing atomic number. If one would remove the Pauli principle from the periodic system all electrons would follow the law of minimum energy and revert to the lowest quantum state $n = 1$, with loss of energy.

In the language of wave mechanics, the Pauli exclusion principle then represents a new restriction of the mathematically possible solutions of the wave equation. Only those solutions are permitted where, owing to the above principle, no repetition of all four quantum numbers occurs. In the following chapters we shall see how this fundamental law will accompany us everywhere, be it in the formation of molecules, or in the electron theory of metals which, applied to the electron gas model in organic molecules, leads to the calculation of energy terms of normal and excited states. The absorption spectra, i.e., the color of organic molecules, may be predicted, based on the above considerations.

CHAPTER 11

Concepts of the Chemical Bond
Prior to the Beginning
of Quantum Mechanics

The problem of the nature of the chemical bond is as old as chemical research itself. In ancient times and in the Middle Ages, efforts were made to explore the nature of the chemical forces based on philosophical considerations. Heraclitus' (535–475 B.C.) statement "All happenings result from an opposition"* lent belief to the concepts about the causes of chemical affinity, namely, that certain materials appear to be attracted to each other, whereas others are completely indifferent towards each other. In modern times this thought obtained its concrete physical form only through Berzelius (1812) who developed the first theory of the chemical bond. This was only several years after Dalton (1808) had replaced the atomic theory of the Greeks with the law of simple and multiple proportions based on experimental facts.

The Berzelius theory of the chemical bond could be stated simply in that two elements combine only if they are carrying opposing electric charges. This law ruled for several decades the field of chemical research. Many facts then known could be well explained because most substances under investigation consisted of inorganic compounds. As we know nowadays, their bonds are based on electrostatic attraction of ions. With further development, particularly in the field of organic chemistry, the Berzelius theory was no longer tenable. For example, if the H atoms in CH_4 were said to carry a positive charge, one could not explain why successive replacement with negative Cl atoms also led to stable compounds. The predicament was even greater when one realized that certain molecules such as H_2, O_2, N_2, etc., are formed of two like atoms having no polarity whatever. This fact was explained away by the name of "homopolar bond." The difficulties in explaining this class of compounds, however, accompanied

---

* Τά πάντα ἐξ ἐναντιότητος γίγνεσθαι.

chemists into the year 1927 and were only solved by Heitler's and London's application of wave mechanical concepts (see Chapter 9).

In the beginning of structure theory, chemical bond formation was likened to two interlocking hooks which united the atoms and these hooks were later replaced by a single straight line, which is still in use nowadays. In the period 1830–1850 the reactions of organic compounds were described by the radical theory of Liebig and Wöhler, and by the substitution theory of Kolbe. Soon scientists learned to determine atomic and molecular weights by physicochemical methods, which contributed considerably to the solidity of the valence concept. Shortly after, LeBel[1a] and van't Hoff[1b] (1879) introduced the directional chemical bond with the description of the C atom as a regular tetrahedron. This made the prediction of the number of isomers and stereoisomers possible. A very fertile hypothesis was born, which resulted in a stormy development of organic chemistry. The constitution of a large number of new organic molecules was proven, and a similar large number of new organic molecules was synthesized. There was little time to think about the character of the chemical bond, since the practical valence bonds expressed in straight lines were sufficient and successful. From a physical viewpoint, however, the representation of valence by straight lines was not very satisfactory, and very soon the insufficiency of this shorthand method was demonstrated. Some examples will point out the difficulties which are encountered in writing valence relationships with single lines.

If the strength of a single C—C bond is represented by a single line, then double bonds C=C should be twice as strong, and triple bonds, C≡C, 3 times as strong as single bonds. If one chooses as a criterion of comparison the strength of the binding energy of the atoms, as they can be calculated from the heats of combustion, one finds that a double bond is only 1.5 times as strong, and a triple bond only 2.3 times as strong as a single bond. The two lines of the double bond hence are no longer of equal value, just as the three lines of the triple bond are unequal. If one wishes to make a statement as to the strength of the bond on the basis of reactivity, for example, the ease with which the bond can be broken, then one observes a much more complicated behavior. The C≡C, with triple bond, adds bromine or hydrogen (in the presence of a catalyst) with great facility and forms a double bond. This compound with double bond combines with H_2

[1a] LeBel, *Bull. soc. chim. France* [2] **22,** 337 (1874); [3] **3,** 788 (1890).

[1b] J. H. van't Hoff, "Die Lagerung der Atome im Raum," 3rd ed. Vieweg, Braunschweig, 1908.

or Br_2 to form a single C—C bond. These two bond types thus impart an unsaturated, highly reactive character which is not found in the single bonds. This then sharply points up the inequality of the various bonds in the double and triple bonds, which is not shown by the lines of the customary shorthand.

The difficulties become even more pronounced in the study of properties of compounds with conjugated double bonds. In the case of butadiene— the simplest representative of a conjugated system of double bonds— bromine addition takes place in the 1,4-position, whereby the double bond migrates into the 2,3-position, according to the scheme:

$$CH_2{=}CH{-}CH{=}CH_2 + Br_2 = BrCH_2{-}CH{=}CH{-}CH_2Br$$

The addition of sodium to butadiene (Ziegler) follows the same course. Thiele tried to explain the nature of the saturation on each C atom by so-called partial valences

$$\rangle CH_2 = CH{-}CH = CH_2$$

which indicated that the reactive nature of double bonds was insufficiently described with regular valence lines. Furthermore, if these bonds form a ring of a certain number of C atoms, as in the case of benzene, a reduction of the unsaturated and reactive state results. This now is termed aromatic character. The manifold phenomena became even more complex through the development of mesomerism. Under this term one summarizes a number of rather complex facts (see Chapter 12). A compound with conjugated double bonds behaves in such a fashion that one ascribes it a structural formula which assumes a not sharply defined position among a number of limiting structures, each of which can be exactly formulated. According to the reagent with which this compound reacts, it seems to do so according to different structural formulas. This would serve to re-emphasize that a rigid theory using straight lines to denote valence is insufficient to account for the experimental facts.

As a first step for a physical foundation of the valence concept, we must familiarize ourselves with the work of Kossel[1c] (1916) and the independently conceived theory of electron shells by Lewis.[2] Both authors

---

[1c] W. Kossel, "Valenzkräfte und Röntgenstrahlen," 2nd ed. Springer, Berlin, 1924.

[2] G. N. Lewis, "Valence and the Structure of Atoms and Molecules." Reinhold, New York, 1923.

started from different premises for the construction of the atoms out of nuclei and electrons and arrived at the same result, whereby the electrons in the atomic bond are arrayed in concentric shells around the nucleus. These shells are considered closed when the electron numbers are 2, 8, 18, and 32. These numbers correspond to particularly stable, and hence preferred, configurations, as they are found in the case of the rare gases which always conclude a period in the system of the elements. If in one element the number of electrons is larger or smaller than the number corresponding to the rare gas configuration, the atoms desire to assume rare gas configuration by capturing or surrendering electrons, thus forming

TABLE 1b

Lattice Energies of the Alkali Halides[a]

	$U_{calc.}$	$U_{exptl.}$
LiCl	193.3	198.1
NaCl	180.4	182.8
KCl	164.4	164.4
RbCl	158.9	160.5
CsCl	148.9	155.1
LiBr	183.1	189.3
NaBr	171.7	173.3
KBr	157.8	156.2
RbBr	152.5	153.3
CsBr	143.5	148.6

[a] Units: kcal/mole^3.

anions or cations, respectively. These ions then form stable compounds owing to electrostatic attraction, and are capable of existence in all states of aggregation. The captured or surrendered electrons are called valence electrons; they determine the charge of the resulting ions and hence the valence with which these atoms undergo "compound" formation.

With this principle, then, all heteropolar compounds, i.e., most compounds belonging in the field of inorganic chemistry, could be put into a rational scheme (see Table 1b). Born,[3] Madelung,[4] and others have applied the Coulomb attraction law to these ions, considered having rigid electron shells, and could calculate the lattice energy of heteropolar solid bodies in good agreement with experience (Table 1b). However, the formation of homopolar or covalent bonds, respectively, still remained unexplained.

---

[3] M. Born, in "Handbuch der Physik" (H. Geiger and K. Scheel, eds.), Vol. XXIV/2. Springer, Berlin, 1933.

[4] E. Madelung, Göttinger Nachr. p. 100 (1909); p. 43 (1910); Physik Z. 11, 898 (1910).

In order to include homopolar bonds into this scheme, Lewis (1916)[5] recognized that the electron configuration of an octet need not be realized by complete surrender or capture of electrons, but could be obtained by the sharing of two electrons among the two ligands resulting in the formation of a bond. In this fashion, two noble gas configurations combine whereby one electron pair belongs to both octets simultaneously. In contrast to electrostatic action, which explains electrovalent bonds, and which is based on a complete transition of one electron from one atom to the other, the covalent bond is based on the sharing of an electron pair. Thus two fluorine atoms each with seven electrons according to the scheme:

$$:\overset{\cdot\cdot}{\underset{\cdot\cdot}{F}}\cdot \ + \ \cdot\overset{\cdot\cdot}{\underset{\cdot\cdot}{F}}: \ = \ :\overset{\cdot\cdot}{\underset{\cdot\cdot}{F}}:\overset{\cdot\cdot}{\underset{\cdot\cdot}{F}}:$$

unite with the formation of two intersecting octets and form the fluorine molecule. In an analogous fashion the four H atoms furnish four electrons to the C having four electrons and form methane

$$\cdot\overset{\cdot}{\underset{\cdot}{C}}\cdot \ + \ 4\cdot H \ = \ \begin{matrix} H \\ H:\overset{\cdot\cdot}{C}:H \\ H \end{matrix}$$

where the outermost electrons of C again show rare gas configuration.

The importance of the new method of writing does not reside in the replacement of the valence line with two dots,* but in the fact that the bond can be treated independently of the nature of the ligands. In the ammonia molecule we can see that the formation of the octet is based on the uniting of three electrons belonging to three hydrogen atoms with three electrons of the nitrogen atom. However, there remains one lone electron pair belong-

$$\cdot\overset{\cdot\cdot}{N}\cdot \ + \ 3\cdot H \ = \ \begin{matrix} H \\ :\overset{\cdot\cdot}{N}:H \\ H \end{matrix}$$

ing to the nitrogen atom without any bond partner. Such electron pairs are able to accept an ion, having no electrons, or atoms with electron gaps (incomplete octets) and thereby form a new covalent bond. The formation of the ammonium ion from NH_3 and H^+ is formulated thus:

---

* After the Pauli principle was applied to homopolar bonds, the postulate that both electrons have antiparallel spins became necessary.

[5] G. N. Lewis, *J. Am. Chem. Soc.* **38,** 762 (1916); W. Kossel, *Ann. Physik* [4] **49,** 229 (1916).

$$
\begin{array}{c}
\text{H} \\
\ddot{} \\
\text{H}:\overset{\displaystyle \cdot\cdot}{\underset{\displaystyle \cdot\cdot}{\text{N}}}: \\
\text{H}
\end{array}
\;+\; \text{H}^+ \;=\;
\left[
\begin{array}{c}
\text{H} \\
\ddot{} \\
\text{H}:\overset{\displaystyle \cdot\cdot}{\underset{\displaystyle \cdot\cdot}{\text{N}}}:\text{H} \\
\text{H}
\end{array}
\right]^{+}
$$

with the formation of a covalent bond where both electrons are furnished by one of the partners, the N of the NH_3 molecule. This is termed coordinate covalent bond (Sidgwick[6a]).

A further advantage for the replacement of the valence line by an electron pair is the simplification in writing the formation of complex salts. Werner[6b] in 1905 introduced the concept of coordinate covalence in order to explain the existence of complex salts. Formation of potassium tetrafluoroborate was formulated as

$$
\text{KF} + \text{BF}_3 \longrightarrow \text{KF}\cdots\text{BF}_3
$$

where one assumed that after the saturation of the three-valent boron by three fluorine atoms a residual valence remains which is responsible for the formation of the addition complex of BF_3 with KF. If one writes this process as a complex formation with the symbolism for electrons (I)

$$
\begin{array}{c}
:\ddot{\text{F}}: \\
:\ddot{\text{F}}:\text{B} \\
:\ddot{\text{F}}:
\end{array}
\;+\; :\ddot{\text{F}}: \;+\; \text{K}^+ \longrightarrow
\left[
\begin{array}{c}
:\ddot{\text{F}}: \\
:\ddot{\text{F}}:\text{B}:\ddot{\text{F}}: \\
:\ddot{\text{F}}:
\end{array}
\right]^{-} \text{K}^+
$$

(I)

one can see that the incomplete octet in boron (electronic gap) is filled by the lone electron pair of the fluorine ion. Formation of two touching complete octets is also responsible for the formation of the complex anion BF_4^-. Hence, the distinction between main and covalence is not really necessary, inasmuch as the combination leading to the complexing of all F atoms of the three original via main valences and the fourth via a covalence produces a complex ion, in which they are all equally bound and hence equivalent.

The double bond was then represented by participation of two atoms with two electron pairs and likewise the triple bond by three electron pairs.

[6a] N. V. Sidgwick, "The Electronic Theory of Valency." Oxford Univ. Press, London and New York, 1927.

[6b] Cf. P. Pfeiffer, "Organische Molekülverbindungen" (Chemie in Einzeldarstellungen, Vol. XI), 2nd ed. Enke, Stuttgart, 1927.

However, this method of writing was still unable to represent the fine distinctions between the various electrons in double and triple bonds, so that here the electron formula did not show an advantage over the valence lines. In contrast to this, the new method of writing proved useful in certain classes of compounds such as the sulfones and sulfoxides, not only in a formal but also in a physical sense. Sulfoxides and sulfones were generally written with the method of valence lines:

$$\begin{array}{ccc} R{\diagdown} & & R{\diagdown}{\diagup}O \\ \quad S=O & or & \quad S \\ R{\diagup} & & R{\diagup}{\diagdown}O \end{array}$$

with four and six valent sulfur, respectively, where in the molecule one or two double bonds, respectively, occur. According to the Lewis formulation, however, the distribution of the electrons is such that octets with one common electron pair are formed so that sulfur in sulfoxides (II) is singly positively and oxygen singly negatively charged. In the neutral state they each contain six outer electrons, and after counting up to combined octets, there must be an electron pair common to both atoms. In sulfoxides one covalent and one ionic bond exist between sulfur and oxygen. Such a composite bond type is called a semipolar bond. It is apparent in the high value of the dipole moment (e.g., 4.44D for diethylsulfone). Here, the charge distributions comprise a whole unit of elementary charge and must not be confused with polarity, as is found in the case of alkyl halides. As the halogens are more electronegative, the shared electron pair tends to be nearer these bond partners.

$$\begin{array}{ccc} & & O^- \\ R\!:\!\overset{+}{\underset{\cdot\cdot}{\overset{\cdot\cdot}{S}}}\!:\!\overset{\cdot\cdot}{\underset{\cdot\cdot}{O}}\!:^- & or & R\!:\!\overset{\cdot\cdot}{\underset{\cdot\cdot}{S}}\!:\!O^+_{\ -} \\ R & & R \end{array}$$

$$(\text{II}) \qquad\qquad (\text{III})$$

By analogy, the sulfur in the sulfones (III) has a double positive charge since it has four electrons, while it has six electrons in the neutral state. Consequently, each oxygen atom has a negative charge and the sulfur–oxygen bond is simultaneously covalent and dipolar. The marked difference between the old and the new method of writing then is found in the absence of double bonds in electronic formulas of sulfones and sulfoxides. A differentiation between these two methods of writing has been made possible by measuring the parachor. The resulting data favor the electronic formula.

The parachor P is a constant characteristic of the liquid state and given by the expression

$$P = \gamma^{1/4} \cdot \frac{M}{D - d} \tag{43}$$

where γ is the surface tension, M the molecular weight, D the specific gravity of the liquid, and d the vapor density. The parachor of a molecule is an additive property and can be calculated from the parachor values of the individual atoms with consideration of the increments for double and triple bonds[7] (cf. Table 2).

TABLE 2
Atomic Parachor Values and Increments[a]

H	17.1	Cl	54.3
C	4.8	Br	68.0
N	12.5	Double bond	23.2
P	37.7	Three-membered ring	16.7
O	20.0	Four-membered ring	11.6
O_2	60.0 (ester)	Five-membered ring	8.5
S	48.2	Six-membered ring	6.1
F	25.7	Triple bond	46.6

[a] From Tables of Parachor Values. A. I. Vogel, *J. Chem. Soc.* p. 1842 (1948).

If one measures the parachor of sulfoxides one realizes that no double bond increments should be applied (methyl sulfate: observed—238.9; calculated—240.4 vs. SO_2Cl_2: observed—193.3; calculated—196.8) so that one must decide in favor of electronic formulas. A similar situation exists in the case of amine oxides. The electron formula indicates a semipolar bond between N and O.

The successful description of a group of phenomena which come about through the formation of hydrogen bonds indicates the progress furnished by the use of electronic formulas. Since the hydrogen atom is particularly small ($r = 0.3$ A) it has the ability to approach other atoms very closely, its bare nucleus touching lone electron pairs and hence producing additional electrostatic attraction forces. In this fashion a hydrogen nucleus can hold two atoms containing lone electron pairs quite firmly together, so that they

[7] S. Sugden, *J. Chem. Soc.* **125,** 1177 (1924); also "The Parachor and Valency." London, 1930; S. Sugden, J. B. Reed, and H. Wilkins, *J. Chem. Soc.* **127,** 1525 (1925); S. A. Mumford and J. W. C. Phillips, *ibid.* p. 155 (1928); p. 2112 (1929); T. W. Gibling, *ibid.* p. 209 (1941); p. 661 (1942); p. 146 (1943).

form a new kinetic unit. The formation of bimolecular hydrogen fluoride is formulated as

$$H:\overset{..}{\underset{..}{F}}: \quad + \quad H:\overset{..}{\underset{..}{F}}: \longrightarrow H:\overset{..}{\underset{..}{F}}:H:\overset{..}{\underset{..}{F}}: \longrightarrow H^+ \quad + \quad \left[HF_2\right]^-$$

and indicates that an H atom forms a bridge between two F⁻ ions. The strength of a hydrogen bridge bond is generally assigned a value between 3 and 10 kcal/mol, while regular covalent bond energies range between 50 and 100 kcal/mol.

By stipulating the existence of such hydrogen bonds, other phenomena can be explained which had been known for a long time under the name of association. They throw light on the character of liquids or liquid mixtures and produce an abnormal decrease in fugacity, or an abnormally high viscosity of substances which contain dissociable H atoms, on the one hand, and atoms with lone electron pairs such as N, O, and F, on the other. Compounds which may form such H-bonds are, e.g., NH_3, H_2O, HF, alcohols, organic acids, etc. The increase in boiling point, in viscosity, and in dielectric constant in comparison with compounds with equally strong polar structure thus comes about by more or less loose addition of molecules via H-bonds according to:

$$CH_3:\overset{..}{\underset{..}{O}}:H \quad + \quad H:\overset{..}{\underset{..}{O}}:CH_3 \longrightarrow CH_3:\overset{..}{\underset{..}{O}}:H:\overset{\overset{\textstyle H}{|}}{\underset{..}{O}}:CH_3$$

Hydrogen bonds may be formed not only between two separated molecules but also between groups belonging to the same molecule. The intramolecular hydrogen bond also leads, as a consequence, to an increase in fugacity as can be shown by comparing the melting points of the three isomers of hydroxybenzaldehyde (IV–VI). The steady increase of boiling

-7°   + 106°   + 116°

(IV)   (V)   (VI)

points from *ortho* to *meta* to *para* isomers can be explained as follows. The *ortho* compound forms an intramolecular hydrogen bond which is not able to undergo intermolecular association and consequently has a lower boiling point. The *para* compound, on the other hand, on account of the large distance between OH and the carbonyl group, can form no internal hydrogen bridge, so that the above groups are free to form H bonds with other molecules leading to association products. The *meta* compound takes an intermediary position. The gradation of melting points of the three isomers of nitrophenol (VII–IX) can be related again in an analogous manner to the

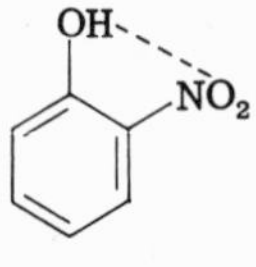

| 45° | 96° | 114° |
| (VII) | (VIII) | (IX) |

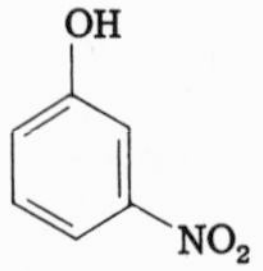

formation or lack of inter- and intramolecular bonds, respectively. In 1-hydroxyanthraquinone

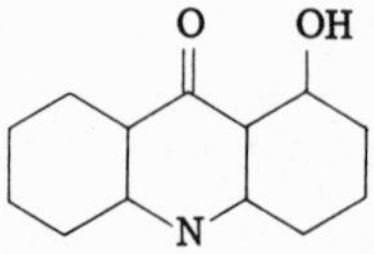

the intramolecular H bond which is characteristic in chelates[8] explains the reduced reactivity of the OH group in methylation or acetylation, respectively. The existence of hydrogen bonds may also be demonstrated spectroscopically by determination of the position of absorption bands in the infrared. The vibration of the hydrogen towards the oxygen in the direction of the tie lines between the nuclei—the so-called OH valence frequency—is dampened owing to H-bond formation by the interaction of the H with a second O atom towards lower frequencies. This is indeed the case as can be shown for formic acid:[9]

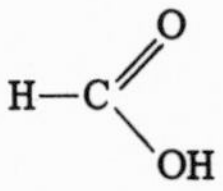

Monomer = 3682 cm^{-1} 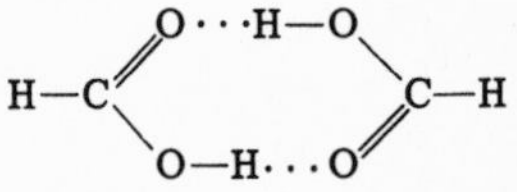   Dimer = 3400 cm^{-1}

---

[8] A. E. Martell and M. Calvin, "Chemistry of the Metal Chelate Compounds." Prentice-Hall, Englewood Cliffs, New Jersey, 1953.

[9] M. M. Davies and G. B. Sutherland, *J. Chem. Phys.* **6,** 755 (1938).

as well as in other compounds.[10,11] Although the forces which cause hydrogen bond formation are essentially of electrostatic nature, a certain portion of it must be ascribed to resonance energy between the two structures

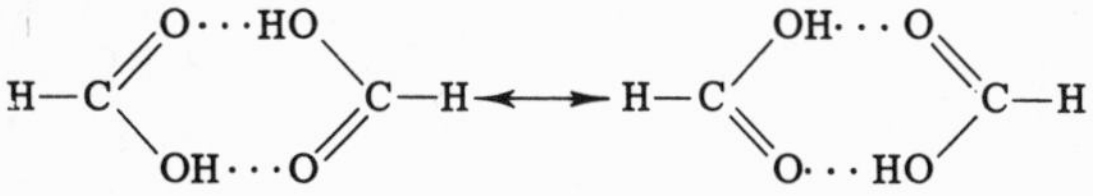

$$H-C\underset{OH\cdots O}{\overset{O\cdots HO}{\diagup\diagdown}}C-H \longleftrightarrow H-C\underset{O\cdots HO}{\overset{OH\cdots O}{\diagup\diagdown}}C-H$$

(see Chapter 12).

Hydrogen, in the case of hydrogen bonds, does not function as a divalent element as might appear at first sight. The electron state of divalent hydrogen would have to be $2s$ or $2p$. This is an energy too large for a stable hydrogen bond. For the hydrogen bond, the polarity of the bond participating with the hydrogen atom is of importance. This can be shown in the decrease of the tendency to H-bond formation in the series

$$HF \;>\; ROH \;>\; R_2NH \;>\; R_3CH$$

which goes hand in hand with a decrease in dipole moment.

H-bonds are of greatest importance in the biological properties of long chain molecules such as proteins. Here H-bonds between the H atom of the NH_2 groups and the O of the $C{=}O$ groups can combine polypeptide chains so that high polymer association networks of the following type

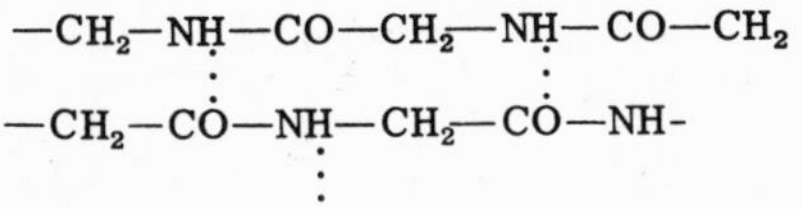

$$-CH_2-\overset{..}{N}H-CO-CH_2-\overset{..}{N}H-CO-CH_2$$
$$-CH_2-\overset{.}{C}O-NH-CH_2-\overset{.}{C}O-NH-$$

result.

---

[10] R. Mecke, *Discussions Faraday Soc.* **9**, 161 (1950).

[11] Existence of dimeric association products is also proved by electron diffraction studies; see L. Pauling and L. O. Brockway, *Proc. Natl. Acad. Sci. U.S.* **20**, 336 (1934); J. Karle and L. O. Brockway, *J. Am. Chem. Soc.* **66**, 574 (1944).

CHAPTER 12

Mesomerism.
Resonance

In the historical development of the structure of organic compounds the discovery of tautomerism plays an important role. Laar[1] and later von Baeyer,[2] as well as numerous other investigators, found that certain organic compounds could be described by two discretely different formulas, depending on their environment. These two formulas correspond to two species which are in chemical equilibrium. Among the classical examples for tautomerism are: acetoacetic ester, *p*-nitrosophenol,[3] and *p*-nitro-phenol.[4] The keto form is in equilibrium with the enol form (the nitro form with the quinoid form) so that according to pH and nature of the solvent, one or the other species can be quantitatively obtained (desmotropism, from the Greek δεσμός = handcuff).

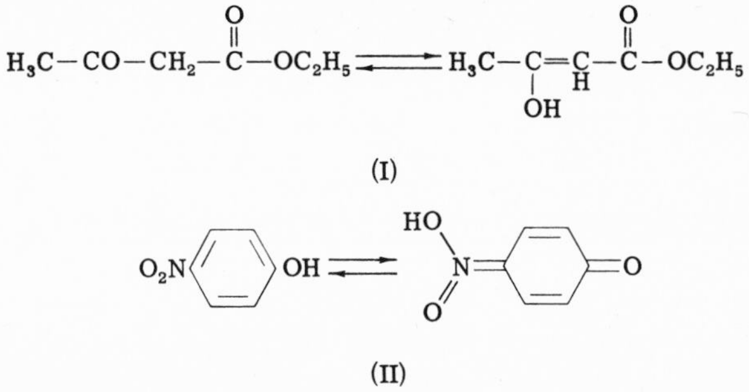

$$H_3C-CO-CH_2-\overset{\overset{O}{\|}}{C}-OC_2H_5 \rightleftharpoons H_3C-\underset{\underset{OH}{|}}{C}=\underset{H}{C}-\overset{\overset{O}{\|}}{C}-OC_2H_5$$

(I)

$$O_2N\!\!\left\langle\!\!\bigcirc\!\!\right\rangle\!\!OH \rightleftharpoons \underset{O}{\overset{HO}{\diagdown}}N\!\!\left\langle\!\!\bigcirc\!\!\right\rangle\!\!=O$$

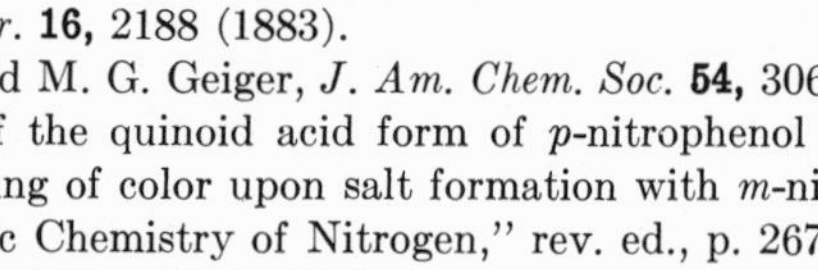

(II)

---

[1] C. Laar, *Ber.* **18,** 648 (1885); **19,** 730 (1886).

[2] A. von Baeyer, *Ber.* **16,** 2188 (1883).

[3] L. C. Anderson and M. G. Geiger, *J. Am. Chem. Soc.* **54,** 3064 (1932).

[4] The correctness of the quinoid acid form of *p*-nitrophenol has been questioned because of the deepening of color upon salt formation with *m*-nitrophenol. See N. V. Sidgwick, "The Organic Chemistry of Nitrogen," rev. ed., p. 267. Oxford Univ. Press (Clarendon), London and New York, 1945.

On the basis of formulas (I) and (II) one finds that tautomerism is always connected with a migration of the proton and a simultaneous shift of the double bond.

In about 1920, however, after many observations, it was found that the behavior of the compounds with conjugated double bonds could not be described by a single formula. Rather, a series of structural formulas without a shift of H or other atoms, but only a change in position of the electrons in the molecule, was required to maintain the doublet or octet configurations, respectively. The structure of the molecule appeared to be not quite sharply defined, but intermediary between these extreme, yet exactly formalized, limiting structures.[5] The phenomenon based on this latter reason was responsible for its name: mesomerism. The principal difference between tautomerism and mesomerism lies in the fact that in mesomerism the positions of all mass points in these limiting structures is the same and only the double bonds, i.e., the electron densities, are shifted. A classical example for the new situation is found in benzene for which two formulas (A) and (B)

(A)   (B)

can be written, differing only in the positions of the double bonds.[6] If benzene could be represented by only formula (A), one should be able to isolate two *ortho* disubstitution products (C) and (D)

(C)   (D)

which would differ according to whether a double bond is present between both *ortho* substituents or not. It is known that Kekulé, in order to escape this difficulty, assumed an oscillation of the double bonds between posi-

[5] C. K. Ingold, *Chem. Revs.* **15**, 225 (1934); F. Arndt and B. Eistert, *Z. physik. Chem.* **B31**, 125 (1936).

[6] G. W. Wheland, "Advanced Organic Chemistry," 3rd ed., p. 90. Wiley, New York, 1960.

tions (A) and (B), which was so rapid that the demonstration of the two limiting (A) and (B) was rendered impossible. It is in this point particularly that the modern concept of mesomerism differs with the older concepts. The quantum mechanical treatment of the problem shows that in the case of benzene one deals not with two molecular species in equilibrium with each other, but with a single state which lies in between the states represented by formulas (A) and (B). Hence, there are no single and double bonds which change in the time interval between the C atoms of the benzene ring, but there exist simultaneously among all C atoms a type of bond which lies in between the double and single bond, say, a one and one-half bond.*

In support of this concept—that there is no dynamic interchange between two limiting states—is the fact that benzene does not undergo the usual bromine addition as do other conjugated double bond systems, but that it forms a triozonide with the more active reagent O_3. Analogous situations are found in more complex compounds with conjugated double bonds. Thus γ-pyrones could be represented according to formula (III)

$$O=\langle\!\!\!\!\!\!\bigcirc\!\!\!\!\!\!\rangle=O$$

(III)

as a diolefin ketone, although typical ketone reactions such as condensation with hydroxylamine are absent, in contrast to the analogously built dibenzal acetone. Thus one is tempted to ascribe the structure of a zwitterion with aromatic character to the γ-pyrones according to formula (IV).

$$^-O—\langle\!\!\!\!\!\!\bigcirc\!\!\!\!\!\!\rangle—O^+$$

(IV)

This structure, however, would lead to a high dipole moment, whereas the actual measured value lies between the values of a zwitterion and a diolefin. On the other hand, one can form a hydrazone with p-nitrophenyl

---

* The modern English school prefers the symbol:

hydrazine, which is a stronger agent for CO groups, and hence accentuate the keto character of the pyrones. If one wanted to indicate all the properties of pyrones with a single formula, one would have to select one which lies between that of the diolefin and the zwitterion. Since such "in-between" states cannot be described with the chemical shorthand, the "in-between" state mesomerism is indicated by a double arrow between the two limiting structures. Thus one speaks about a mesomeric electron distribution in the

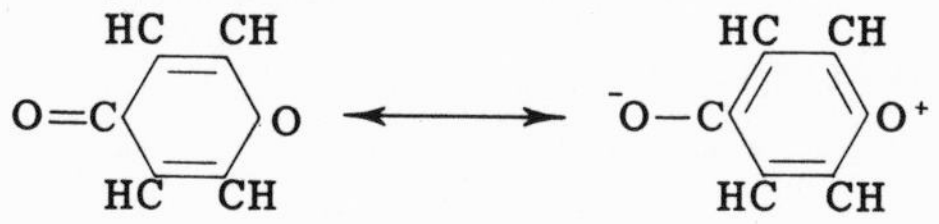

(V)

limiting formula of a stable "in-between" state which cannot be drawn but which is a mental construct.

Similarly, a much used expression refers to resonance "between" structures (A) and (B). This, however, could easily lead to a misunderstanding, as if there were a secret coupling mechanism between two physical entities in the case of the Kekulé limiting formulas. This is not the case and the molecule is represented only by a single state. The name resonance is derived from a wave mechanical treatment of the bond mechanism of the two electrons in the helium atom,[7] which was also used in the treatment of the H_2 problem. It is a mathematical treatment and not a physical phenomenon. In the next chapter it will be shown in which way it can be applied to conjugated double bonds.

---

[7] W. Heisenberg, Z. *Physik* **39**, 499 (1926).

CHAPTER 13

The Valence Bond (VB) and Molecular Orbital (MO) Methods*

The wave mechanical treatment of the stable mesomeric state can be carried out according to two different methods—the valence bond and the molecular orbital method—two methods of calculation which lead to essentially the same results. Using the valence bond method (Slater,[1] Pauling[2]) one writes all structural formulas obtainable by shifting electrons, and calculates from their superposition the resonance hybrid which is energetically lower than any of the contributing structures. The calculation is based, in the main, on the relative weights with which the individual above-mentioned limiting structures are contained in the resonance hybrid. This mixing is carried out by the formation of linear combinations of wave functions for the individual structures and equating them with the wave function of the hybrid according to

$$\psi = c_1\psi_1 + c_2\psi_2 + c_3\psi_3 \cdots c_n\psi_n. \tag{44}$$

The weights of the structures are equal to the square of the coefficients $c_1, c_2, c_3, \ldots, c_n$, which are varied in such a way that the energy E of the resulting wave function ψ takes the lowest possible value (variation method). This is a necessary condition for the stability of the resonance

* Cf. E. Cartmell and G. W. A. Fowles, "Valency and Molecular Structure." Academic Press, New York, 1956; J. D. Roberts, "Notes on Molecular Orbital Calculations," W. A. Benjamin, New York, 1961.

[1] J. C. Slater, *Phys. Rev.* **38**, 1109 (1931).

[2] L. Pauling, *J. Chem. Phys.* **1**, 280 (1933); G. W. Wheland, *ibid.* **23**, 79 (1955); R. McWeeny, *Proc. Roy. Soc.* **A223**, 63, 306 (1954); **A227**, 288 (1955).

hybrid. Since the energy of a valence structure is obtainable* from its wave function

$$E = \frac{\int \psi H \psi d\tau}{\int \psi^2 d\tau},$$ (45)

the energy of the resonance hybrid in the case of benzene can be represented as contributions of the two Kekulé structures (A) and (B) in an analogous fashion by:

$$E = \frac{c_1^2 H_{11} + 2c_1 c_2 H_{12} + c_2^2 H_{22}}{c_1^2 S_{11} + 2c_1 c_2 S_{12} + c_2^2 S_{22}}$$ (46)

if

$$\int \psi_1 H \psi_1 d\tau = H_{11}$$ (47)

and

$$\int \psi_1 \psi_1 d\tau = S_{11}$$ (48)

are substituted.† In order to obtain the coefficients c_1, c_2, etc., which correspond to the lowest energy value, one forms the partial derivatives $\partial E/\partial c_1$, $\partial E/\partial c_2$, etc., and sets them equal to 0. This leads to the so-called secular equations:

$$c_1(H_{11} - ES_{11}) + c_2(H_{12} - ES_{12}) = 0$$
$$c_1(H_{12} - ES_{12}) + c(H_{22} - ES_{22}) = 0.$$ (49)

In the formation of the linear combinations of the wave functions, it is important that the resulting wave function of the disturbed system should not correspond to a value of an energy which is intermediate between the energy values of the contributing weight functions, but to one which is lower than the lowest energy value of the combining structure.[3] The difference between the energy value of the hybrid and the lowest energy value of one of the structures, from which it has resulted, is called reso-

---

* In quantum mechanics H is called the Hamiltonian operator, obtained from the classical Hamiltonian functions in which the momentum is replaced by

$$\frac{h}{2\pi i} \cdot \frac{\partial}{\partial x}.$$

† In the case of complex functions one of the ψ-functions in the integrand has to be replaced by the complex conjugate ψ^*.

[3] F. Hund, "Einführung in die Theoretische Physik," Vol. 7, p. 369. Bibliogr. Inst., Leipzig, 1956.

nance energy, according to Pauling. It is larger, the greater the number of the individual contributing structures and the smaller their energy differences. One can prove this in the case of benzene by first using only the two Kekulé structures and then improving the calculation by considering the three Dewar structures in Eq. (44) (I–III). In the former case

(I)   (II)   (III)

one calculates the stabilizing resonance energy of the molecule as $0.9J = 30$ kcal, in the second case as $1.106J = 36$ kcal. The latter value is very close to the experimental one. However, each of the Dewar structures only contributes 1/6 as much as each of the Kekulé structures. Consideration of further structures, such as a polar one, would not lead to any essential stabilization with subsequent increase in resonance energy because the contributing weights of polar structures are very small. The number of structures one should consider with respect to weighting the function is given by the number of combinations in which the π electrons with opposite spin can be paired. It is equal to the number of line formulas which can be obtained without crossovers. From this, covalent molecule structures result with a total spin of 0. The number of combinations of permitted structures is equal to

$$\frac{(2n)!}{n!(n+1)!} \tag{50}$$

where $2n$ denotes the number of π electrons. It is shown in Table 3 that in aromatic compounds this number grows rapidly with an increasing number

TABLE 3
Covalent Structures with Increasing Double Bonds

Compound	Number of π electrons	Number of covalent structures from Eq. (50)
Butadiene	4	2
Benzene	6	5
Naphthalene	10	42
Biphenyl	12	132
Anthracene	14	234

of π electrons. It is also seen that consideration of all structures becomes complicated quite rapidly with the number of conjugated double bonds.

It must be stressed that, according to the valence bond method, the canonical structures do not have the character of a physical hypothesis but are only a mathematical dodge. In contrast with a physical hypothesis, their physical reality in this case must not be postulated because of its successful application, but rather one is led to conclude the nonexistence of the cited structures. The only physical realities are the resulting resonance hybrids, following the mathematical combination process.

If one follows the calculation of this principle which has been called the "approximation of complete pairing," one is led to:

$$E = E_\sigma + \frac{Q + J}{1 \pm S^2} \tag{51}$$

which is formed in analogy to the energy equations for the H_2 molecule, (38) and (39). In this equation the first term E_σ refers to the electron energy of the σ bonds and the second to the energy of the π electrons. Here Q stands for the Coulomb integral, J for the exchange integral, and S for the overlap integral as they were introduced in Chapter 9 with the terms C, A, and S for the special case of the hydrogen molecule. Here, too, the exchange integral J is of overriding importance for the stabilization of the molecule. We shall investigate its influence in contrast with the contribution in the Kekulé and Dewar structures. For this one neglects the overlap integral assuming it is 0, and considers only the interaction of immediately neighboring π electrons. At a random orientation of π electrons, parallel and antiparallel spin orientation should occur with equal probability. The exchange integral has a value of $-J$ at parallel orientation of spins and a value of $+J$ at antiparallel orientation. Since parallel orientation according to the three directions in space occurs 3 times (triple degeneracy) and antiparallel only once, the most probable total value of the integral J in the random orientation of π electrons is given by the algebraic summation

$$3(-\tfrac{1}{4}J) + \tfrac{1}{4}J = -\tfrac{1}{2}J.$$

A nonrandom orientation of π electrons with respect to each other is concomitant with localization of double bonds in benzene so that the total exchange energy in the molecule with an arbitrary number of π electrons is given by summation of the exchange integrals:

$$E_{\text{exch}} = \sum J_{ij} \quad - \quad \sum J_{ij} \quad - \quad \sum \tfrac{1}{2} J_{ij}.$$

$$\downarrow \uparrow \qquad\qquad \uparrow \uparrow \qquad\qquad \downarrow \uparrow$$

$$\text{paired} \qquad \text{unpaired} \qquad \text{random}$$

For a Kekulé structure, one calculates the energy of the π electrons as:

$$E_{\text{Kek}} = Q + 3J + 3(-\tfrac{1}{2}J) = Q + 1.5J$$

and for a Dewar structure, where the exchange integral between electrons and positions 1 and 4 is neglected:

$$E_{\text{Dew}} = Q + [2J + 4(-\tfrac{1}{2}J)] = Q.$$

Thus it is shown since J is negative, that the Dewar structure is richer in energy by the amount $1.5J$. It contributes correspondingly a lesser amount to the resonance hybrid. The statistical weight of each Kekulé structure is ascribed 0.8 and each Dewar structure 0.2.

In contrast to the above treatment of the VB method, the other (MO) method starts with the weight functions of the individual nonbonded atoms and their atomic orbitals (AO), which interact with each other through delocalization of the electrons which finally "melt" into the mesomeric state. This method thus makes no assumption of certain "superposition" of resonance structures, which then have to be declared as not possible of real existence but as mathematical dodges. Rather, the calculation follows the principles which we have discussed in the treatment of the covalent bond, where the molecule is produced as the energetically lowest state obtainable from the atomic orbitals. In the MO method, the delocalization of the electron did not lead to the superposition of discrete structures as in the valence bond method, but to a coalition of atomic orbitals into molecular orbitals. The mixing of the AO's is based on the principle of linear combination, obtained by varying the coefficient of a molecular electronic state (MO) whose energy value corresponds to a minimum.*

The calculation for the benzene molecule is now carried out as follows: Each of the six π electrons ($2p$ state) is considered as if it moved in the field of the remaining molecule consisting of nuclei and all other electrons.[4,5] In this field there is attraction of the delocalized electron as well as repulsion furnished by the other π electrons. The resulting molecular orbital is

---

* According to a proposal by Mulliken one terms this method LCAO method (Linear Combination of Atomic Orbitals).

[4] Self-consistent field method of D. R. Hartree, *Proc. Cambridge Phil. Soc.* **24**, 89 (1928); *Repts. Progr. in Phys.* **11**, 113 (1946–1947).

[5] E. Hückel, *Z. Physik* **70**, 204 (1931).

formed and represented by the linear combination of the wave function
of the six individual π electrons:

$$\psi = c_1\psi_1 + c_2\psi_2 \ldots c_6\psi_6. \tag{52}$$

The coefficients c_1, c_2, $\cdots$, c_6, are given by six secular equations as shown
above. With the simplifying assumptions that all overlap integrals are 0
and that the resonance integral (coupling integral)

$$\beta = \int \psi_r \mathbf{H} \psi_s d\tau \tag{53}$$

need only be considered between two neighboring atoms r and s, one obtains
for the six secular equations the determinant:

$$\begin{vmatrix} Q-E & \beta & 0 & 0 & 0 & \beta \\ \beta & Q-E & \beta & 0 & 0 & 0 \\ 0 & \beta & Q-E & \beta & 0 & 0 \\ 0 & 0 & \beta & Q-E & \beta & 0 \\ 0 & 0 & 0 & \beta & Q-E & \beta \\ \beta & 0 & 0 & 0 & \beta & Q-E \end{vmatrix} = 0. \tag{54}$$

A determinant of this type does not apply to benzene alone but quite
generally for molecules with more than two π electrons, in that its rows are
adapted to the number of π electrons. A general solution leads to

$$Q - E = -2\beta \cos (2\pi j/n) \tag{55}$$

where n is the number of π electrons and j a series of numbers from 1, 2,
3, . . . to n. This equation therefore furnishes n solutions. In the present
case of the benzene molecule one obtains the following six solutions:

(1) $Q + 2\beta$ ($\uparrow \downarrow$)   (4) $Q - \beta$ (0)

(2) $Q + \beta$ ($\uparrow \downarrow$)   (5) $Q - \beta$ (0)

(3) $Q + \beta$ ($\uparrow \downarrow$)   (6) $Q - 2\beta$ (0)

These six solutions correspond, however, to only four different energy
states since solutions 2 and 3, as well as 4 and 5, are equal, and hence
represent doubly degenerate energy states. The next step consists of feeding to each of these states two electrons of opposite spin (Pauli principle).
This procedure is carried out starting with the lowest energy term, which
is the $Q + 2\beta$ state since β has a negative value. The first three solutions
correspond to the bonding molecular orbitals, since their energy value is

less than Q, whereas the remaining three solutions with energy values higher than Q represent the antibonding molecular orbitals. They remain unoccupied in this case.

If one wishes to make a quantitative statement about the stability of the benzene nucleus, based on the delocalization of the π electrons from the Kekulé structures to a mesomeric state, one has to subtract from the total energy of the π electrons in the mesomeric state:

$$2(Q + 2\beta) + 4(Q + \beta) = 6Q + 8\beta$$

the energy of the six π electrons in the localized state of the Kekulé structure, i.e., $6Q + 6\beta$. The difference of 2β then would be the stabilization energy of benzene resulting from resonance.

Although the term β is similar to the exchange integral J of the VB method, it differs from it numerically. The resonance energy of benzene, determined according to the VB method, amounts to $1.106J$, whereas if one uses the MO method as mentioned above one obtains 2β. The ratio of β/J here, as in a series of hydrocarbons with conjugated double bonds, has a constant value of 0.54. The reason for this apparent discrepancy between

TABLE 4

Resonance Energies According to VB and MO Methods

Compound	Resonance energy	
	VB method	MO method
Benzene	$1.106J = 36.8$ kcal/mol	$2.00\beta = 36$ kcal/mol
Naphthalene	$2.04J = 68.2$	$3.86\beta = 66$
Anthracene	$2.95J = 99$	$5.32\beta = 96.3$
Phenanthrene	$3.02J = 101$	$5.45\beta = 98.0$
Biphenyl	$2.37J = 79.6$	$4.38\beta = 78.9$
Butadiene	$0.23J = 7.7$	$0.47\beta = 8.5$
Hexatriene	$0.46J = 16.1$	$0.99\beta = 17.8$
	$J = 33.5$ kcal/mol	$\beta = 18$ kcal/mol

the two integrals seems to lie in the fact that the integral J refers to the exchange energy of two electrons between two atomic orbitals, whereas β is an expression for the exchange of one π electron between two atomic orbitals. Comparatively speaking, J would correspond to the resonance between two electrons in the H_2 molecule, while β indicates resonance of one electron between the two protons in the H_2^+ ion. Indeed, one finds for the ratio of bond energies of H_2^+/H_2 a value of 0.59.

Table 4 summarizes the resonance energies of some important hydrocarbons calculated on the basis of the VB and the MO method.[6]

The agreement between both methods is quite satisfactory. Yet considerable differences with experimental data are apparent, in comparison with Tables 5 and 6 in Chapter 14.

---

[6] C. A. Coulson, "Valence." Oxford Univ. Press (Clarendon), London and New York, 1952.

Resonance, Coplanarity, and Steric Hindrance

The value of the resonance energy can be determined experimentally, permitting comparison of theory with experimental facts. The principle on which the determination of resonance energy is based is shown schematically in Figure 11. The heavier line indicates the energy level of the

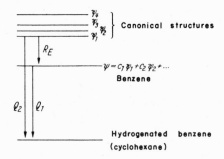

Fig. 11. Definition of resonance energy according to Pauling.

mesomeric or hybridized molecule, obtained by linear combination of the eigenfunctions ψ_1, ψ_2, ψ_3, . . . of the canonical structures lying above. According to Pauling the difference between the energetically lowest canonical structure and the energy level of the resonance hybrid is termed R_E. If these two states are combined in a common state, such as the completely hydrogenated molecule, which no longer can exhibit mesomerism, the difference in heats of hydrogenation of the above structures is the resonance energy. The mesomeric state can be directly hydrogenated since this is the existing molecule. On the other hand, a hydrogenation of the energetically lowest canonical structure can only be arrived at indirectly or by calculation, since, as stated above, the canonical structures cannot exist per se but are mathematical figments. One can, however, proceed in such a fashion that, for the hydrogenation of the lowest canonical structure, one uses a closely related substance where the double bonds are localized. With a suitable calculation it can then be related to the fictitious canonical structure. In the case of benzene one calculates the heat of hydrogenation of one of the nonexisting canonical Kekulé structures from the heat of hydrogenation of cyclohexene which has one double bond which is necessarily localized. By multiplying this heat of hydrogenation with a factor of 3 one obtains the heat of hydrogenation of one Kekulé structure. Since the heat of hydrogenation of cyclohexene is 28.59 kcal/mol one arrives at the heat of hydrogenation of the hypothetical Kekulé structure with a value of $3 \times 28.59 = 85.77$ kcal/mol. On the other hand, the heat of hydrogenation of benzene, viz., the resonance hybrid, was determined at 49.80 kcal/mol. From the difference one then calculates the resonance energy at 35.97 kcal/mol.

Since the heats of hydrogenation are not easily measured, owing to the slowness of the process, one makes use of the heats of combustion in arriving at the resonance energy values. The heats of combustion are generally easily ascertained, although the bond energies necessary for their calculation may often be somewhat uncertain because they are obtained as differences of large calorie numbers. The resonance energies of a series of compounds with single and double bonds, obtained by the two methods of calculation as well as experimentally, are summarized in Tables 5 and 6. One notes that the heats of hydrogenation of olefins are reasonably constant, with a value of 30 kcal/mol for each double bond. In contrast, the heats of hydrogenation of compounds with conjugated double bonds are lower than would be obtained by multiplying the double bond value with the number of occurrences ($n \times 30$ kcal/mol). The stabilization resulting from conjugation had already been pointed out by Thiele and has been treated in detail. From the numerical values of the resonance energy one notes that this quantity becomes larger with increasing number of double bonds, i.e., with increasing number of π electrons. The resonance energy of benzene ($R_E = 36$) increases in going to naphthalene ($R_E = 61$) and to higher condensed hydrocarbons such as chrysene ($R_E = 116.5$). The 1,3,5-triphenylbenzene molecule shows a stabilizing energy of no less than 149 kcal/mol.

One must not expect a direct parallelism between resonance energy and stability of the molecule in a reaction-kinetical sense. Admittedly, naphthalene is more reactive than benzene toward certain reagents, yet

TABLE 5[a]
Resonance Energies of Some Mesomeric Compounds

Compound	Heat of hydrogenation— observed (kcal/mol)	Heat of hydrogenation— calculated (kcal/mol)	Resonance energy (kcal/mol)
Ethylene	32.8	—	—
Propylene	30.1	—	—
cis-2-Butene	28.6	—	—
trans-2-Butene	27.6	—	—
Cyclopentene	26.9	—	—
Cyclohexene	28.6	—	—
Tetramethylethylene	26.6	—	—
1,3-Butadiene	57.1	60.6	3.5
1,3-Cyclohexadiene	55.4	57.2	1.8
1,3,5-Cycloheptatriene	72.8	79.5	6.7
Benzene	49.8	85.8	36.0
Ethylbenzene	48.9	84.1	35.2
o-Xylene	47.3	82.4	35.1
Mesitylene	47.6	80.7	33.1
Styrene	77.5	114.4	36.9
Furane	36.6	53.8	17.2
Vinylether	57.2	60.6	3.4
Ethylvinylether	26.7	30.3	3.6

[a] Values shown are taken from G. W. Wheland, "Resonance in Organic Chemistry," p. 78. Wiley, New York, 1955.

its resonance energy is about twice that of benzene. On the other hand, a certain parallelism is shown in the example of p-quinone which has a small resonance energy corresponding to its unsaturated reactive character.

One can liken the spreading of the electrons over the whole molecule with its conjugated double bonds by delocalization with the adiabatic expansion of an ideal gas. As in the case of a gas, the π electrons in the adiabatical extension over the total system of double bonds suffer a decrease of their energy content. This expansion can only take place if all involved atoms lie in one plane. If the centers of gravity of the atoms in a molecule form angles with each other, then the process of adiabatic expansion leading to an energy minimum cannot take place. We arrive, in this way, at an interesting stereochemical conclusion regarding mesomerism. The mesomeric molecule must be planar. For the molecules benzene, naphthalene, anthracene, etc., this is quite well established on the basis of

TABLE 6[a]

Resonance Energies of Some Mesomeric Compounds

Compound	Heat of combustion— observed (kcal/mol)	Heat of combustion— calculated[b] (kcal/mol)	Resonance energy (kcal/mol)
1,3-Butadiene	608.5	611.5	3.0
1,3-Cyclopentadiene	707.7	709.3	1.6
Benzene	789.1	825.1	36.0
Toluene	943.6	979.0	35.4
o-Xylene	1098.5	1133.6	35.1
Mesitylene	1252.5	1286.8	34.3
Hexamethylbenzene	1726.3	1752.7	26.4
Stilbene	1718.5	1858.4	76.9
Biphenyl	1513.7	1584.7	71.0
Fluorene	1608.0	1683.9	75.9
1,3,5-Triphenylbenzene	2955.0	3103.9	148.9
Phenylacetylene	1034	1068.7	35
Diphenylacetylene	1756	1827.6	72
Naphthalene	1249.7	1310.7	61.0
Anthracene	1712.1	1795.6	83.5
Phenanthrene	1705.0	1796.3	91.3
Chrysene	2165.8	2282.3	116.5
Furane	506.9	522.7	15.8
Thiophene	612.0	640.7	28.7
Pyrrole	578.0	599.2	21.2
Aniline	823.8	862	38
α-Naphthylamine	1283.6	1348	64
Benzoquinone	671.5	676	4
Formic acid	75.7	88	12
Acetic acid	220	233	13
Benzoic acid	791	838	47
Urea	172	202	30
Cyclooctatetraene	1095	1099	4
Azulene	1279	1312	33
Tropolone	826	847	21

[a] Values shown are taken from G. W. Wheland, "Resonance in Organic Chemistry," p. 98. Wiley, New York, 1955.

[b] F. Klages, *Ber.* **82,** 385 (1949).

their structural formulas and x-ray investigations. In the carboxylic acids, mesomerism takes place by a charge exchange between the two oxygens in the manner:

$$-C\overset{\displaystyle O}{\underset{\displaystyle O^-}{\Big\langle}} \quad\longleftrightarrow\quad -C\overset{\displaystyle O^-}{\underset{\displaystyle O}{\Big\langle}}$$

The resonance energy of benzoic acid (67 kcal/mol) exceeds the sum of the resonance energies of benzene (35.9 kcal/mol) and formic acid, HCOOH, (18 kcal/mol) by more than 10 kcal/mol.[1] This additional amount may be ascribed to the interaction of the π electrons of the phenyl radical with the lone electron pairs of the oxygen atoms of the carboxyl group, as both moieties lie in one plane. However, the numerical data are too uncertain to provide a conclusive proof.

If deviations from coplanarity are observed, they generally go hand in hand with a lack in resonance. They may arise through the fact that steric hindrance prohibits a planar molecular accommodation of the atoms, which, as we have seen, is an important steric premise for resonance stabilization. We shall illustrate this fundamental principle in the physical chemical behavior of organic molecules with conjugated double bonds.

If one introduces a CH_2 group into the benzene ring and thus obtains cycloheptatriene (I) the number of the π electrons and the corresponding

$$\underset{\text{(I)}}{\begin{array}{c}\quad\quad H\quad\;\; H\\ \quad\quad C=C\\ \diagup\quad\quad\;\;\diagdown CH\\ H_2C\quad\quad\quad\;\;\|\\ \diagdown\quad\quad\;\;\diagup CH\\ \quad\quad C=C\\ \quad\quad H\quad\;\; H\end{array}}$$

number of canonical structures remains the same as with benzene. However, the resonance energy decreases to the small amount of 6.7 kcal/mol. Consequently, the above compound no longer possesses aromatic character and is quite reactive. The molecule cannot be planar owing to the tetrahedral orientation of the introduced CH_2 group.

However, if one changes the cycloheptatriene ring into a cation, there results a more stable system with a certain degree of aromaticity, as was shown by Doering and Knox who synthesized cycloheptatrienyl bromide,[2] also called tropylium bromide (II). This finding throws light on the problem

---

[1] Numerical values taken from G. W. Wheland, "The Theory of Resonance," p. 69. Wiley, New York, 1947.

[2] W. von E. Doering and L. Knox, *J. Am. Chem. Soc.* **76,** 3203 (1954).

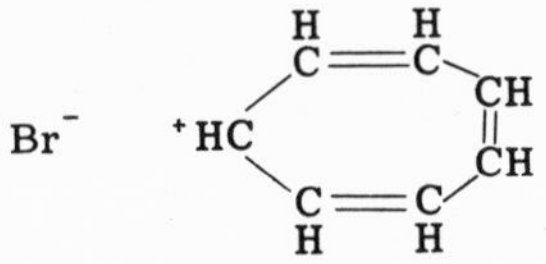

(II)

of the stability of tropolone,[3] which has in many respects aromatic character

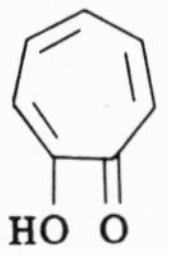

even though its resonance energy only amounts to 21 kcal. For example, it reacts with phenol in undergoing coupling reactions.

The premise of coplanarity is not fulfilled in the case of cycloocta-tetraene (III) because eight carbon atoms with three valence bonds cannot

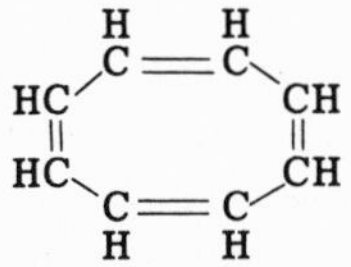

(III)

each form an angle of 120° with each other, without resulting in considerable strain in the formation of an eight-membered ring. Therefore the cyclo-octatetraene molecule does not show the peculiarities of the aromatic hydro-carbons, but behaves like an olefin regarding its unsaturation.[4] It readily adds bromine and is rapidly oxidized with permanganate. In a planar molecule the angle would have to be 135°. Correspondingly, if one wished to maintain the trigonal symmetry of the valences around the C atoms with an angle of 120°, the molecule would no longer be planar. The next highest cyclic hydrocarbon with conjugated double bonds which can be constructed strain-free[5] is the $C_{18}H_{18}$ molecule (IV). It has been synthe-sized recently.[6]

[3] J. W. Cook and J. D. Loudon, *Quart. Revs. (London)* **5,** 99 (1951).

[4] R. Willstätter and E. Waser, *Ber.* **44,** 3423 (1911); R. Willstätter and M. Heidel-berger, *ibid.* **46,** 517 (1913); W. Reppe, O. Schlichting, K. Klager, and T. Toepel, *Ann.* **560,** 1 (1948); cf. K. Ziegler and H. Wilms, *ibid.* **567,** 27 (1950).

[5] O. E. Polansky, *Monatsh.* **91,** 203, 887, 890, 916 (1960).

[6] F. Sondheimer and R. Wolovsky, *J. Am. Chem. Soc.* **81,** 1771 (1959).

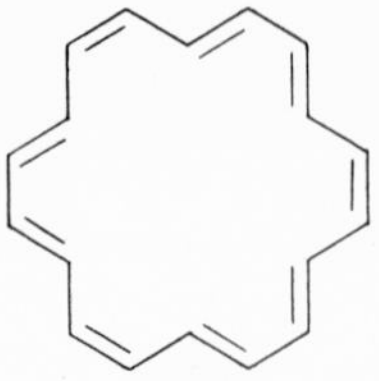

(IV)

Wherever coplanarity of the molecular skeleton is possible, aromatic character is found when the number of the π electrons is $4n + 2$, with n assuming values of 1, 2, 3, 4, ... For $n = 1$ the low energy aromatic sextet is formed which is realized in the neutral molecules benzene, thiophene, pyridine, pyrrole, as well as in the cyclopentadienyl anion and the cycloheptatrienyl cation. In analogy one encounters an aromatic character for $n = 2$ with naphthalene (ten π electrons) and for $n = 3$ with anthracene and phenanthrene (fourteen π electrons). But this (Hückel's Rule) cannot be a general rule, as shown in the example of the planar fulvene, an isomer of benzene, which behaves like an olefin.

The coplanarity can be disturbed by introduction of bulky substituents. This results in a lack of stabilization resonance. In the case of *cis*-stilbene (V) one finds no additional resonance energy exceeding the value for two

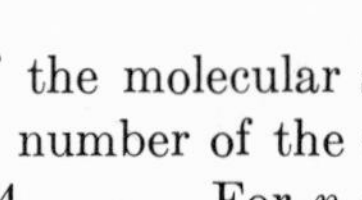

(V)

phenyl rings, because these two substituents cannot assume a coplanar orientation. They must be twisted with respect to each other. In contrast to this in the case of *trans*-stilbene, a resonance energy of 7 kcal/mol is found, in agreement with the fact that here the phenyl rings do not disturb each other and are lying in a plane.

From these examples one sees that the postulate for coplanarity is energetically not so strong that it cannot be abolished by certain factors such as the bulk of substituents. In the biphenyl molecule, the two phenyl groups are coplanar so that the π electron clouds of the groups overlap each other. This is concluded, based on the fact that the resonance energy of biphenyl exceeds twice the value of the resonance energy of benzene.* However, if one introduces NO_2 or CH_3 groups into the *ortho*-position, the coplanar orientation of the two phenyl rings is no longer possible. They must be twisted towards each other. Proof of this is found in the existence of optically active isomers of dinitrodiphenic acid (VI). In these cases, the

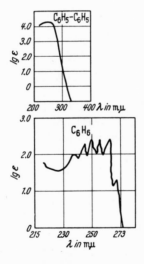

d and l, respectively $[\alpha]_D \pm 127°$

(VI)

additional resonance increment of the stabilization energy is lacking.

The reduction of coplanarity through steric inhibition can also be followed by a study of the ultraviolet spectra.[8] Biphenyl shows its own charac-

FIG. 12. Ultraviolet absorption spectra of benzene and biphenyl.

---

* Electron diffraction experiments with gaseous biphenyl[7] indicate however that the two phenyl rings are twisted against each other like a screw with a 45° ± 10° angle.

[7] O. Bastiansen, *Acta Chem. Scand.* **3,** 408 (1949).

[8] E. Merkel and C. Wiegand, *Z. Naturforsch.* **3b,** 93 (1948); cf. W. Theilacker, G. Kortüm, and G. Friedheim, *Chem. Ber.* **83,** 508 (1950); cf. also E. A. Braude, *Experientia* **11,** 457 (1955).

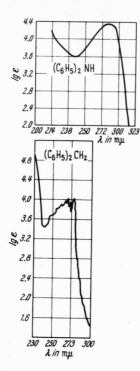

Fig. 13. Ultraviolet spectra of diphenylamine and diphenyl methane.

teristic spectrum in the ultraviolet range which differs markedly from that of benzene (Fig. 12). In dimesityl (VII), however, the absorption of benzene reappears and it shows the absorption bands of mesitylene (VIII) enhanced

(VII)   (VIII)

by a factor of 2. These differences are explained stereochemically so that in the planar configuration of biphenyl, the π electrons of the two phenyl rings overlap, leading to other energy terms, and hence to a different absorption spectrum. In contrast, a coplanar position of the phenyl groups is impossible in dimesityl, owing to steric hindrance of the *ortho*-methyl substituents. The overlapping of π electrons is abolished and therefore the absorption spectrum of benzene reappears. A proof for this stereochemical conclusion is the fact that 3,3'-diaminodimesityl (IX) behaves in a similar

d and l, respectively $[\alpha]_D \approx 42°$

(IX)

fashion to the dinitrodiphenic acid and can be resolved into the optical enantiomorphs. This, however, is only possible if the molecule does not possess a plane of symmetry, i.e., in this case if both phenyl groups are twisted towards each other. Substitution of biphenyl in the *meta* or *para* position, respectively, does not produce any effects of this kind.

The absence of mesomeric electron shifts, prohibited by sterical factors, can also be followed in studying acid dissociation constants.[9] In the stereoisomeric olefin carboxylic acids, the dissociation constant of the *cis* compound (relative position of a substituent to the carboxyl group) is always higher than in the corresponding *trans* compound. *cis*-Cinnamic acid has a dissociation constant of 13.2×10^{-5} whereas the value for the *trans* acid only amounts to 3.65×10^{-5}. These gradations are explained by a deviation of the sterical arrangement from a planar array, owing to the steric hindrance in the *cis* compounds. In the *trans* compounds, because of the planar arrangement of the substituents, a mesomeric electron shift may take place, particularly directed towards the O atom of the COOH group. As the O becomes more negative, it makes the dissociation of the proton more difficult. In the same category of electron displacement effects one encounters another, rather weak effect which is connected with the presence of terminal methyl groups and their donor properties. It has become known under the term hyperconjugation. We shall discuss this effect after we have clarified the relationships between bond character and atomic distances.

[9] H. C. Brown, D. H. McDaniel, and O. Häfliger, *in* "Determination of Organic Structures by Physical Methods" (E. A. Braude and F. C. Nachod, eds.), Vol. I, p. 567. Academic Press, New York, 1955.

CHAPTER 15

Hybridization

The electron distribution of various atomic states which were discussed in Chapter 8 hold, strictly speaking, only for isolated atoms. They correspond to the case of very dilute gases where mutual interaction can be neglected. In the solid state we must take into account a disturbance of the electron cloud which leads to a broadening of the discrete energy states. This is shown schematically in Fig. 14 where the widening of the energy

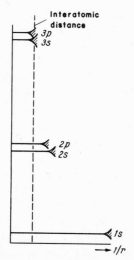

FIG. 14. Broadening of energy terms.

level is plotted as a function of the mutual distance r of two atoms. This broadening can lead to complete overlapping of energy bands in the metallic state and hence produce a continuous blending of the states. A blending of electron states must also be assumed in isolated atoms such as the C atom, if one wants to take into account its valence behavior. If we write the electronic states of the C atom using the nomenclature of Chapter 8, we arrive at the following scheme:

$$\underbrace{(1s) \; \Updownarrow}_{K} \qquad \underbrace{(2s) \; \Updownarrow \; (2p_x) \uparrow \; (2p_y) \uparrow \; (2p_z).}_{L}$$

The first, K shell, is occupied by two electrons of opposing spin in the spherical distribution in space. It is considered completed since it cannot accept any additional electrons. The second, L shell, is occupied with two different kinds of electrons, one $2s$ pair and two $2p$ electrons which are distributed with parallel spin among the x and y states (Hund's rule). This rule states that in a given configuration, the lowest energy state corresponds to the highest multiplicity compatible with the Pauli exclusion principle. The $2p_z$ state remains unoccupied (no arrows). Since the electrons of the outer shell are responsible for the chemical valence, carbon correspondingly should be tetravalent with respect to the four outer valence electrons, yet should have two dissimilar types of valence.[1] This is in contradiction with experience since it has been proven that all four valences of the C atom are equal and that they have a well defined direction in space, forming a regular tetrahedron with mutual angles of 109°. Hence one must conclude[2] that the C atom, prior to undergoing covalent bonding, must rearrange its electron states. This process is carried out in two steps. One electron of the $2s$ state is promoted to the unoccupied $2p_z$ state whereby an energy of 96 kcal/mol is expended. The resulting state is shown by the following scheme:

$$(2s) \uparrow \; (2p_x) \uparrow \; (2p_y) \uparrow \; (2p_z) \uparrow \,,$$

i.e., four electrons with the same direction of spin are distributed among four states. In the second step the four different electron clouds are mixed to form four equal electron clouds of mixed character, also termed hybrid. This process of mixing or hybridization leads to four equal valence hybrids having a well defined direction in space. In the present case, the mixing of a $2s$ electron with three $2p$ electrons results in four sp hybrids of tetrahedral arrangement. The mixing is carried out mathematically by combining the four original wave functions ψ_{2s}, ψ_{2p_x}, ψ_{2p_y}, and ψ_{2p_z} of the above four states linearly with the proper selection of suitable coefficients a_1, b_1,

---

[1] Cf. K. Artmann, *Z. Naturforsch.* **1**, 426 (1946), where tetrahedral and trigonal arrangements are stipulated for free atoms as a corollary to the Pauli exclusion principle.

[2] L. Pauling, *J. Am. Chem. Soc.* **53**, 1367 (1931); **54**, 992 (1932).

c_1, d_1, a_2, b_2, c_2, d_2, etc. respectively. This results in four new ψ functions, ψ_1, ψ_2, ψ_3, ψ_4, which are completely equivalent but which have different spatial direction.

$$\psi_1 = a_1\psi_{2s} + b_1\psi_{2p_x} + c_1\psi_{2p_y} + d_1\psi_{2p_z},$$

$$\psi_2 = a_2\psi_{2s} + b_2\psi_{2p_x} + c_2\psi_{2p_y} + d_2\psi_{2p_z},$$

$$\psi_3 = a_3\psi_{2s} + b_3\psi_{2p_x} + c_3\psi_{2p_y} + d_3\psi_{2p_z},$$

$$\psi_4 = a_4\psi_{2s} + b_4\psi_{2p_x} + c_4\psi_{2p_y} + d_4\psi_{2p_z}.$$

In deriving these four new wave functions, which are orthogonal to each other,* there exists the following condition: they must be of such a nature that their combination leads to the formation of a covalent bond with an H atom or with another C valence hybrid which maintains maximum overlap of their electron clouds. Maximum overlap leads to a maximum strength

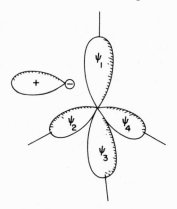

Fig. 15. Electron density distribution in the sp^3 hybrids.

of the bond. This fact indeed justifies and explains the expense of energy of 96 kcal/mol which had been spent in the beginning of the hybridization. Without any additional assumptions, the calculation indicates that the four equivalent sp^3 hybrids are directed towards the corners of a regular tetrahedron. Figure 15 shows the form of the sp^3 valence hybrids of carbon. Aside from their spatial direction they are completely equivalent. The vector character of the sp^3 hybrid is evident also in the polarity of a CH

---

* Two functions ψ_A and ψ_B are orthogonal if their overlap integral has the value 0, i.e., if $\int \psi_A\psi_B d\tau = 0$.

bond in the tetrahedral CH_4 molecule where the bond moment is of the order of $0.3D$.[3] The direction of the dipole moment is from the C to the H atom, i.e., C is more positive than H, in contrast to the expectation based on the greater electronegativity of the C atom. In the sp^2 and sp hybrids (vide infra) the vector of the CH dipole moment shows probably a higher s-content of the bond from the H to the C atom.

If such an sp^3 hybrid overlaps with a second sp^3 hybrid, or with a $1s$ electron of an H atom, a covalent C—C or C—H bond results, which has a cylindrical electron distribution with respect to its axis. This in turn means that rotation of the atoms around this axis does not result in any special configuration because the degree of overlap remains the same for a complete turn. In the parlance of organic chemistry it means that free rotation must exist around a C—C axis. Such cylindrically symmetric electron overlaps, which lead to covalent bonds, are referred to as σ bonds. These relationships and particularly the electronic concept of the double bond were already formulated in 1930 by Hückel.[4]

The above mixing of ψ wave functions resulting in the formation of a sp^3 hybrid is not the only possible one. If one combines the three functions ψ_{2s}, ψ_{2p_x}, and ψ_{2p_y} linearly and permits the fourth ψ_{2p_z} to remain as such, one arrives at a new hybrid state. It consists of three mutually equivalent sp^2 valence hybrids which are trigonal and in one plane, plus a $2p_z$ electron having a perpendicular distribution to the plane of the sp^2 hybrids. It has the shape of a dumbbell. The designation sp^2 should remind us that the new valence is the result of the mixing of the wave function of a $1s$ electron with the wave functions of two $2p$ electrons. The form of this electronic combination with respect to spatial distribution can be seen in Fig. 16a. An angle of 120° is formed between the three sp^2 hybrids which lie in a plane. If one connects two sp^2 hybrids to a covalent bond, there results on the one hand through the overlap of two sp^2 electron clouds a symmetrical distribution (σ bond), and on the other hand a combination of two p_z electron clouds which do not surrender their symmetry character. A nodal plane separates the positive from the negative domains of the wave function (Fig. 16b).

This latter overlap displays an antisymmetrical distribution of the electronic charge and is called a π bond. Both of these bonds thus constitute

[3] C. A. Coulson, "Valence." Oxford Univ. Press (Clarendon), London and New York, 1952; W. L. G. Gent, *Quart. Revs. (London)* **2**, 383 (1948).

[4] E. Hückel, *Z. Physik* **60**, 423 (1930); **70**, 205 (1931); *Z. Elektrochem.* **36**, 641 (1930); **61**, 866 (1957).

the prototype of double bond. A double bond therefore is formed by combination of a σ and a π bond. The latter with its free electrons lends the characteristic properties to the double bond, namely, the character of unsaturation and the rigidity with respect to rotation of the atoms around the C—C axis. It gives rise to the formation of *cis* and *trans* isomers. Free rotation is no longer possible on account of the above-described π electron distribution which constitutes a plane fixed by the two trigonal *sp* hybrids. Rotation of the C atoms around this axis would change the electron distribution and would produce unequal positions during rotation. This in

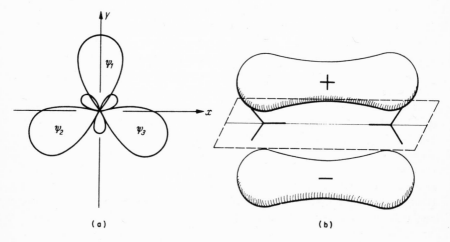

(a)   (b)

FIG. 16.(a) Electron density distribution in the sp^2 hybrids. (b) Molecular orbital of a π bond.

turn would change the degree of overlap. Since this can only happen by furnishing energy, it is concomitant with cleavage of the bond. One can readily see that this type of electron distribution along the tie line between two C—C atoms represents the behavior of a double bond quite satisfactorily. Its strength—it is stronger than a single and weaker than two single bonds—is explained by the combination of a σ and a π bond. Its unsaturation is explained by the π electrons which are coupled only through antiparallel spin. The charge distribution of this electron pair forms a nodal plane which coincides with the plane of the C—C skeleton and accounts for the known rigidity of the double bond.

Finally it is possible to combine a $2s$-ψ function with a $2p$-ψ function linearly leading to two equivalent sp hybrids (Fig. 17). The two remaining $2p_y$ and $2p_z$ electrons remain free. Its distribution in space can be likened to two mutually perpendicular dumbbells with a common node in the middle. Overlap of electron clouds of two such sp hybrids produces a σ and two π bonds. The latter are produced by the coalescence of $2p_y$ and $2p_z$ electrons without any change in symmetry. This is the prototype of a triple bond. Although the rotation of the atoms around the C—C axis is not possible without considerable expense of energy, no *cis-trans* isomers can result because the two sp hybrids form an angle of 180° with each other.

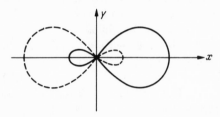

FIG. 17. Electron density distribution in the sp hybrids.

In a covalent bond of two such hybrids, the four atoms lie on a line along its axis of bonds. This corresponds with experience in that *cis-trans* isomers have never been found in acetylene derivatives. On the other hand, the strength of a triple bond is larger than that of two single bonds and its character of unsaturation is more pronounced than that of a double bond.

Hybridization of valence electrons is not restricted to the C atom but can also take place with other elements. It leads to an understanding of the maximum valence of the electrons and their stereochemical behavior. In the case of beryllium, one of its $2s$ electrons is promoted to the $2p_x$ state to form two sp hybrids which are linear in arrangement. In the case of boron with the following electronic state:

$$(2s) \updownarrow\uparrow (2p_x) \uparrow (2p_y)^0 (2p_z)^0,$$

The mixing leads to two sp^2 hybrids, after one $2s$ electron has been promoted to the unoccupied $2p_y$ state. As in the case of the carbon atom, they lie in a plane and form an angle of 120° with each other. The required energy is obtained by maximum overlap in the formation of a bond with a participating atom. Beryllium as well as boron compounds with two or three equal substituents, respectively, do not possess a dipole moment. This is in agreement with the linear or trigonal symmetry of their respective valences.

With tetrahedral hybridization of carbon one reaches a valence of 4. It can be shown that it is not possible to increase this valence in the case of nitrogen, the next element, to 5. The N atom has an electron configuration:

$$(2s) \mathbin{\uparrow\downarrow} (2p_x) \uparrow (2p_y) \uparrow (2p_z) \uparrow$$

in which three electrons are in the three $2p$ states which can overlap with the electrons of combining atoms without previous hybridization. The resulting compound has the form of a flat pyramid. The nitrogen with its two electrons occupies the top. If one wanted to produce pentavalent nitrogen by separating the electron pair and promoting one electron into the $3s$ state, one would need a much larger amount of energy. Such energy could not be recovered in the combination with other elements. The $3s$ energy level is considerably higher than that of the $2p$ states. Hence one cannot hybridize five electrons in nitrogen in order to produce five equivalent valence hybrids, as the energy content of at least one of them would be markedly different. This type of hybridization does not take place and explains the nonexistence of NCl_5. We are led to the conclusion that covalence in the elements of the first period cannot exceed the value of 4 because only $2s$ and $2p$ states exist. This does not, however, hold for the case of phosphorus, the corresponding element of the next higher period. The electron configuration of phosphorus is:

$$(2s) \mathbin{\uparrow\downarrow} (2p_x) \mathbin{\uparrow\downarrow} (2p_y) \mathbin{\uparrow\downarrow} (2p_z) \mathbin{\uparrow\downarrow} ; \quad (3s) \mathbin{\uparrow\downarrow} (3p_x) \uparrow (3p_y) \uparrow (3p_z) \uparrow (3d)^0.$$

It possesses a complete L shell with eight electrons and an M shell with two $3s$ and three $3p$ electrons. The latter three are permitted to have a valence of three. Since the quantum state three is not completely occupied, one of the $3s$ electrons can be promoted with a small expense of energy to the unoccupied $3d$ state. The five single, equidirected electrons can be hybridized to five equivalent sp^3d hybrids:

$$(3s) \uparrow (3p_x) \uparrow (3p_y) \uparrow (3p_z) \uparrow (3d) \uparrow .$$

This bipyramidal arrangement is realized in the very stable PCl_5. Similar arguments must hold for the pentaphenyl phosphorus, $(C_6H_5)_5P$, first synthesized by Wittig.[5]

In the case of the transition elements, iron, cobalt, and nickel, whose $4s$ and $3d$ states have approximately equal energies, mixing of electron character is possible, leading to a higher covalent state. In the Co atom,

---

[5] G. Wittig, *Ann.* **562,** 187 (1949).

mixing of the s, p, and d states produces 6 equivalent sp^3d^2 hybrids which are oriented towards the corners of a regular octahedron. The same type of hybridization and ability to higher covalent configuration is encountered in the cobalt hexamine complexes $[Co(NH_3)_6]^{3+}$. The formation of this complex can be visualized as follows: the Co^{3+} ion lacks the two outer $4s$ and one inner $3d$ electrons (see Table 1a). Each entering NH_3 molecule furnishes one electron from the $2s$ state and changes in turn into an sp^3 tetrahedral hybrid, similar to the positively charged NH_4^+ ion. Of the twelve electrons furnished to the cobalt, six occupy the $3d$ state. The remaining six, through mixing with vacant $4s$ and $4p$ states, occupy the six equivalent sp^3d^2 hybrids, oriented towards the corners of a regular octahedron. Saturation of the six sp^3 valences of the $6(NH_3)^+$ leads to six octahedral σ bonds[6] in the complex cation.

In the elements nickel, platinum, and palladium, in the complexes $[NiCN_4]^-$ and $[PtCl_4]^-$, a tetragonal hybridization is encountered. The four sp^2d hybrids are directed towards the corners of a square, so that the molecule has a planar configuration. This has been proven by the synthesis of *cis-trans* isomers. According to the theory (Pauling) such isomers would not be possible in a tetrahedral arrangement. The examples demonstrate that an essential prerequisite for mixing of electronic states is the approximate equivalence of energy contents.

The transition metals are capable of forming coordination compounds with unsaturated hydrocarbons. Aside from the compounds of platinum and cobalt with olefins and acetylenes, such as $[(C_2H_4)PtCl_3]^-$ and $C_2H_4Co_2(CO)_6$, one may cite the compounds formed between heavy metals and cyclopentadiene and benzene. In some instances the structure has been established. In ferrocene and in chromobenzene the metal atom is sand-

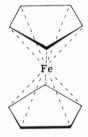 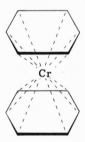

---

[6] For an extensive treatment of bonds in the formation of complex salts, see L. E. Orgel, "An Introduction to Transition Metal Chemistry, Ligand Field Theory." Wiley, New York, 1960.

wiched between two parallel oriented hydrocarbons.[7] This structure, however, does not hold true for all such types as is demonstrated by the fact that dicyclopentadienyl beryllium has a dipole moment. This would argue against a symmetrical arrangement for $(C_5H_6)_2Be$. Insight into the type of bond in the simpler cases is afforded by application of the ligand field theory.[8,9]

---

[7] E. O. Fischer and H. P. Fritz, *Advances in Inorg. Chem. Radiochem.* **1**, 55 (1959).

[8] J. S. Griffith, "The Theory of Transition-Metal-Ions." Cambridge Univ. Press, London and New York, 1961.

[9] L. E. Orgel, "An Introduction to Transition Metal Chemistry, Ligand Field Theory." Wiley, New York, 1960.

CHAPTER 16

Bond Order and Atomic Distance

We have learned from the hybridization theory to differentiate between single, double, and triple bonds and we can express bond character and bond strength through the number of electrons which participate. The bond order is defined as the number of electrons per atom which produce the corresponding bond. A σ C—C bond has the bond order of 1, a double bond which is constituted of a σ and a π bond has a bond order of 2, and a bond containing one σ and two π bonds—a triple bond—has the bond order 3, corresponding to the 2, 4, and 6 electrons, respectively. The usefulness of such a concept is recognized in the more complex molecules, particularly those having conjugated double bonds, where the bond character is not constant, owing to electron shifts, but varies within a certain domain depending on the kind of conjugation and the nature of substituents.

Benzene with its three double bonds, which are distributed among a skeleton of six σ bonds, has a bond order of 1.5 for each C—C bond.* In graphite the bond order is 1.33. A connection should exist between the number of electrons and the bond strength, so that a higher bond order indicates a greater over-all bond strength. On the other hand, one should expect that with increasing bond strength the atomic distances become smaller. Indeed, such a connection exists, as is shown in Fig. 18, which is based on experimental data. This empirical curve, which also has been derived theoretically, shows that the distance between two C atoms changes in a regular fashion from a value of 1.53 A in ethane (bond order 1) to the value of 1.20 A in acetylene (bond order 3). The measurement of the distance of two C atoms then permits a conclusion on the bond order and thereby the number of electrons participating in the bond. This number need not be a whole number which indicates that single, double, and triple

---

* Compare below the values furnished by the VB and MO methods which differ but little from each other.

bonds can exist with a continuous change in charge distribution in many compounds.

After these connections had been realized, many investigations for the determination of atomic distances in organic molecules were carried out. There are four methods which have been used for this purpose: the x-ray diffraction for solid materials,[1] electron diffraction in the vapor state,[2]

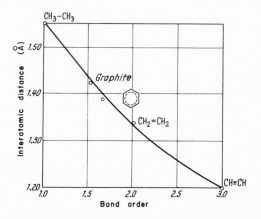

FIG. 18. Dependence of C—C distance on the bond order.

analysis of fine structure in the infrared spectra,[3,4] and microwave spectroscopy.[5,6] A table of atomic distances and atomic angles for a large number of compounds (data including 1954) has been furnished by Wheland.[7] We shall discuss some of these interesting results below.

In diamond as well as in ethane the C—C distance is 1.54 Å. In the compounds acetonitrile, CH_3CN, methyl acetylene, $CH_3C{\equiv}CH$, and diketopiperazine, the C—C distance has values of 1.49, 1.46, and 1.47 Å

[1] J. M. Bijvoet, N. H. Kolkmeijer, and C. H. MacGillavry, "Röntgenanalyse von Kristallen," 1940; see "X-Ray Analysis of Crystals." Butterworths, London, 1951.

[2] L. O. Brockway, in "Physical Methods of Organic Chemistry," Technique of Org. Chem. Ser., Vol. I (A. Weissberger, ed.), Part 2. Interscience, New York, 1949.

[3] G. Herzberg, "Spectra of Diatomic Molecules," Molecular Spectra and Molecular Structure Ser., Vol. I, 2nd ed. Van Nostrand, Princeton, New Jersey, 1956.

[4] D. H. Whiffen, Quart. Revs. (London) 4, 131 (1950).

[5] W. Gordy, Revs. Modern Phys. 20, 668 (1948).

[6] W. Maier, Ergeb. exakt. Naturw. 24, 275 (1951).

[7] G. W. Wheland, "Resonance in Organic Chemistry," p. 695. Wiley, New York, 1955.

$$
\begin{array}{c}
\overset{\text{H}_2 \quad \text{O}}{\underset{\displaystyle}{\overset{\displaystyle}{\text{C}}}\text{---}\text{C}} \\
\text{HN}\diagup \qquad \diagdown \text{NH} \\
\diagdown \text{C}\text{---}\text{C} \diagup \\
\text{O} \quad \text{H}_2
\end{array}
$$

(average error ± 0.02 Å). Based on the curve (Fig. 18) one finds that the bond order in the latter case is 1.3. In other words, 2.6 and not 2 electrons hold this C—C bond together. Consequently, in the above compounds, one does not deal with a single bond but rather with one which lies between a single and a double bond. The excess 0.6 electrons over the number 2 for a single bond must result from the neighboring double and triple bonds, respectively, and is distributed over the C—C bond.

Benzene has been investigated very accurately with the electron diffraction method. It was found that the C—C atoms have a uniform distance of 1.39 A. Also, from the curve in Fig. 18 the bond order in benzene can be read as 1.53. This agrees with the sixfold symmetry (point group D_{6h}) obtained from x-ray data as well as with the other resonance phenomena already mentioned. In order to justify these facts one should write the formula for benzene as follows:

In butadiene, the distance of the two center carbon atoms is decreased to 1.46 because of the neighboring two double bonds and their spreading π electron clouds. In diacetylene, the center bond distance is further decreased to 1.36 A. In contrast to this the CH_3—C distance in hexamethylbenzene is the normal value (1.54) of a single bond. This indirectly supports the argument for the absence of a true double bond in benzene since otherwise the neighboring bonds should be shortened.

The dependence of the distance of two atoms from the number of electrons which contribute to their bond, i.e., bond order, is not restricted to the carbon atom but can also be found with atoms of other elements. The atomic distances of some elements in single, double, and triple bonds are summarized in Table 7. The CN distance in acetonitrile is found to be 1.47 Å whereas in diazomethane CH_2N_2 it is 1.34 Å. It has been shortened by the neighboring multiple N—N bonds. In urea the CN distance is 1.37. This bond takes an intermediary position between a single and a double bond owing to the electron exchange process with the neighboring CO double bond. In methylisocyanate, $CH_3N{=}C{=}O$, the action of the two double bonds upon the CN distance is still larger. It amounts to only 1.18 Å. As

TABLE 7

	Å.		Å.		Å.
C—N	1.47	N—N	1.40	C—Cl	1.76
C=N	1.28	N=N	1.20	—	—
C≡N	1.15	N≡N	1.10	—	—

an example of the shortening of the atomic distance by neighboring double and triple bonds in other element combinations, one might refer to the C—Cl distance in the compounds chlorobenzene C_6H_5Cl (1.69 Å), vinyl chloride $CH_2{=}CHCl$ (1.69 Å), phosgene $COCl_2$ (1.67 Å), in contrast with the C—Cl distance in aliphatic compounds (1.75 Å).

In the butadiene molecule the following distance relationships are found:

$$H_2C{=}CH{-}CH{=}CH_2$$
$$1.39 \quad 1.46 \quad 1.35$$

With the above-mentioned shortening of atomic distance an elongation of the C=C bond takes place. This distance equalization parallels the distribution of the electron density between the C atom and its bond order. A single bond obtains a certain double bond character, whereas the two double bonds suffer a certain loss in double bond character. This transport of a fraction of electronic charge from the position of a double bond can be followed in such compounds as p,p'-aminonitrostilbene (I)

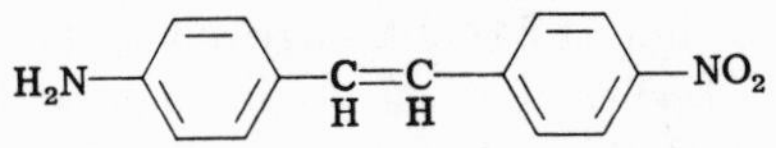

(I)

or indigo (II)

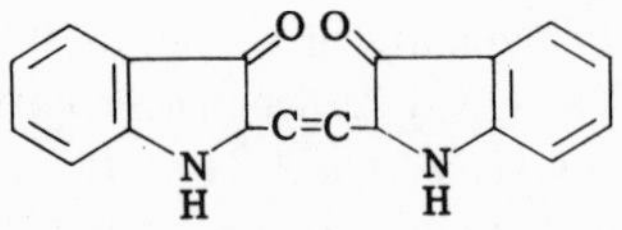

(II)

An isolation of the possible *cis-trans* isomers, owing to the rapid interchange of the two isomers, has not been successful.[8,9] The double bond with respect to its apparent free rotation is similar to a single bond. In the case of indigo, however, a *trans*-orientation appears more likely owing to intramolecular hydrogen bonds between the NH and CO group.[10]

If one extends the polyene chain, the atomic distances become more equalized, as can be seen in the formula for octatetraene

$$H_2C = C - C = C - C = C - C = CH_2$$

with H atoms on each carbon and distances 1.35 1.42 1.37 1.41 1.37 1.42 1.35

In the extended long chain polyenes, the C—C distances approach a limiting value of 1.39 as has been shown in the calculations of Lennard-Jones[11] and Coulson.[12] This corresponds to the C—C distance in benzene and is indeed found in the center of the polyene molecule. Experimentally, this equalization is mirrored in the facile interchange of *cis-trans* isomers and in the frequency position of the Raman lines with increasing chain length. These frequencies move towards lower positions and thus indicate that the force constant of the C—C vibration assumes values between the single $(4.5 \times 10^5$ dyne/cm) and double $(15.6 \times 10^5$ dyne/cm) bond.*

According to a proposal of Pauling, one uses the term percent double bond character in a single C—C bond, depending on its distance between

TABLE 8

Compound	Per cent double bond character	Compound	Per cent double bond character
Benzene	50	Butadiene	75
Graphite	33	Cyclopentadiene	18
Naphthalene	38	Glyoxal	15
Biphenyl	12.5		

* On the other hand, calculations of Kuhn and Platt lead to alternating bond distances in long-chain polyenes; cf. also Longuet-Higgins *et al.*[13]

[8] M. Calvin and R. E. Buckles, *J. Am. Chem. Soc.* **62**, 3324 (1940).

[9] G. Heller, *Ber.* **72**, 1858 (1939).

[10] W. R. Brode, E. G. Pearson, and G. M. Wyman, *J. Am. Chem. Soc.* **76**, 1036 (1954).

[11] J. E. Lennard-Jones, *Proc. Roy. Soc.* **A158**, 280 (1937).

[12] C. A. Coulson, *Proc. Roy. Soc.* **A169**, 413 (1939).

[13] H. C. Longuet-Higgins and L. Salem, *Proc. Roy. Soc.* **A251**, 172 (1959); **A255**, 435 (1960).

a single and a double bond. In Table 8 some numerical values of the per cent double bond character are summarized for some compounds.

Hyperconjugation. A large number of experimental data dealing with the introduction of CH_3 groups into unsaturated compounds can be explained by the fact that the CH_3 group possesses electron donor properties. It becomes apparent in small additional amounts of resonance energy which are found if a CH_3 group replaces a hydrogen directly adjacent to a double or a triple bond. The resonance energy of toluene for example is 1.5 kcal larger than the one of benzene. The resonance energy of *trans*-dimethylethylene

$$H_3C\diagdown \qquad \diagup H$$
$$C = C$$
$$H \diagup \qquad \diagdown CH_3$$

is 5.2 kcal larger than that of ethylene. This fact is ascribed to the conjugation effect of a CH_3 group with a phenyl radical or the double bond of ethylene respectively.[14] The shift in charge must take place from the CH_3 group towards the phenyl ring, i.e., it must be positive with respect to it, as can be verified by dipole moment data. The dipole moment of toluene (0.4 D) is additive to the one of nitrobenzene (4.0 D) in *p*-nitrotoluene (4.5 D) so that both vectors must be in the same direction. Since it is known that the NO_2 group is an electron acceptor, the above addition of partial moments of CH_3 and NO_2 groups in *para*-position is only possible if the CH_3 group is a donor. Since there are no π electrons which could overlap with the π electrons of the phenyl group and yet conjugation takes place, this effect has been called hyperconjugation.[15] It must be due to the nature of the ($1s$-sp^3) bond of the CH_3 group, and particularly to the vector properties of the sp^3 hybrid which has a high percentage of *p*-character. The $2p$ electron distribution has the same symmetry as a π bond so that combination of both charge clouds can take place and therefore amounts to conjugation. The phenomenon of hyperconjugation can be explained by the VB method as more or less probable, limiting structures. It can also be demonstrated with the MO method. Coulson[16] has shown that one of the three possible combinations of atomic orbitals of the CH atoms, the $\psi_I - \frac{1}{2}[\psi_{II} + \psi_{III}]$ combination, leads to a spatial distribution of molecular

---

[14] J. W. Baker and W. S. Nathan, *J. Chem. Soc.* p. 1844 (1935); Conf. on Hyperconjugation, Indiana Univ., Bloomington, *Tetrahedron* **5**, 107 (1959).

[15] R. S. Mulliken, *J. Chem. Phys.* **7**, 339 (1939).

[16] C. A. Coulson, *Quart. Revs. (London)* **1**, 144 (1947).

orbitals (Fig. 19) which has great similarity with the one for π orbitals. In combination with the p-character of the sp^3 hybrid one can lump together the three H atoms of the methyl into one group and write a triple bond with the C atom: $H_3{\equiv}C{-}$. Thus, delocalization of electrons of a CH_3 group

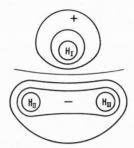

FIG. 19. Electron density distribution of the CH_3 group.

and overlap with other conjugated double bonds is possible. As a sequel of this conjugation, a shortened atomic distance between a CH_3 group and a C atom, neighboring to a double or triple bond, must be expected. It is demonstrated in the case of methyl acetylene where the $CH_3{-}C$ distance

$$H_3C-C{\equiv}CH$$
$$1.46$$

is found to be 1.46 A ("normal" ethane distance = 1.54 A), although the corresponding elongation of the triple bond which should suffer loss

TABLE 9

Ethane	$H_3C{-}CH_3$
	1.54
Ethylene	$H_2C{=}CH_2$
	1.34
Acetylene	$HC{\equiv}CH$
	1.20
Methylacetylene	$H_3{\equiv}C{-}C{\equiv}C{-}H$
	1.46 1.20
Dimethylacetylene	$H_3{\equiv}C{-}C{\equiv}C{-}C{\equiv}H_3$
	1.74 1.20 1.47
Dimethyldiacetylene	$H_3{\equiv}C{-}C{\equiv}C{-}C{\equiv}C{-}C{\equiv}H_3$
	1.47 1.20 1.38 1.20 1.47
Acetaldehyde	$H_3{\equiv}C{-}CH{=}O$
	1.50 1.22
Acetonitrile	$H_3{\equiv}C{-}C{\equiv}N$
	1.49 1.16

of electron charge in hyperconjugation cannot be ascertained.[17] In Table 9 the effect of hyperconjugation on atomic distances is summarized. Aside from the described conjugation between a methyl group and a π electron system, hyperconjugation of the first kind, one can also postulate hyperconjugation of a second kind which should take place among neighboring CH_3 groups according to the scheme shown for ethane:

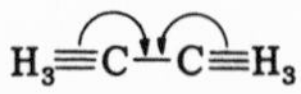

$$H_3 \equiv C \overset{\frown}{\underset{\smile}{\text{{\tiny II}}}} C \equiv H_3$$

It is not possible to estimate this very small influence, since this type of hyperconjugation is almost always present in CH_2 groups and since a reference system for comparison is lacking. Other effects which change hybridization, and therefore change the electronegativity of groups are more pronounced and obscure the effect of hyperconjugation,[18] so that a certain amount of restraint in the interpretation of the data would be indicated. The gradation of ionization potentials of methylated ethylenes (Table 10) cannot be ascribed to the hyperconjugation along. The observed differences in the replacement of an H atom by a methyl group are three to four times larger than should be expected on account of hyperconjugation alone.

TABLE 10

Ionization Potentials

Compound	e. v.
$H_2C=CH_2$	10.62
$H_3C-CH=CH_2$	9.84
$(CH_3)_2C=CH_2$	9.35
trans-$CH_3CH=CHCH_3$	9.27
$(CH_3)_2C=CHCH_3$	8.85
$(CH_3)_2C=C(CH_3)_2$	8.30

Even though the relations are more complicated because the ionization potential is the energy difference between the neutral ground state and the ionized molecule, Hartmann and Svendson[19] were able to show that the inductive effect of the double bond on the substituents accounts for 90% of the observed energy difference.

---

[17] J. W. Baker, "Hyperconjugation," Oxford Univ. Press, London and New York, 1952; F. Becker, Z. angew. Chem. **65**, 97 (1953).

[18] Cf. W. M. Schubert and W. A. Sweeney, J. Org. Chem. **21**, 119 (1956).

[19] M. Svendson, Ph.D. Dissertation, Frankfurt, 1952.

The CH_2 group also has the ability for hyperconjugation although in a lesser degree. This can be shown in the treatment of the resonance problem of cyclopentadiene which for this purpose is written as follows:

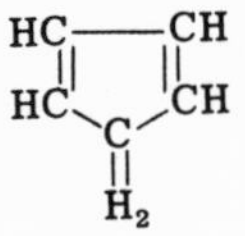

$$\begin{array}{c} HC\!\!-\!\!\!-\!\!\!-\!\!CH \\ \parallel \quad \parallel \\ HC \diagdown{}_{C}\diagup CH \\ \parallel \\ H_2 \end{array}$$

The $C{=}H_2$ group has only a quasi-π electron since only one antisymmetric π function can emerge from the linear combination of the atomic orbitals of the two H atoms. This is in contrast to the CH_3 group which can produce two such quasi-π states. Correspondingly, the resonance contribution of hyperconjugation of the CH_2 group is only half of that of the methyl group.

The conjugation of the CH_3 group with the π electrons of an unsaturated molecule has a profound effect on reaction velocities. The reaction rate of quaternary pyridinium salts from p-alkyl substituted benzyl bromide and pyridine according to

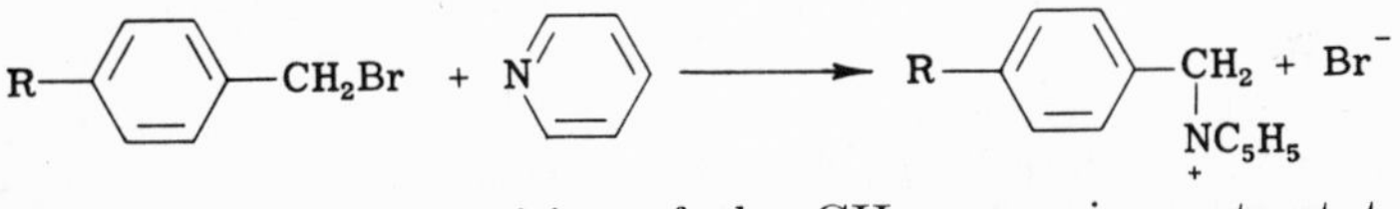

$$R\!-\!\!\!\bigcirc\!\!\!-\!CH_2Br \ + \ N\!\bigcirc \ \longrightarrow \ R\!-\!\!\!\bigcirc\!\!\!-\!\!\underset{\underset{+}{NC_5H_5}}{CH_2} + \ Br^-$$

emphasizes the special position of the CH_3 group in contrast to R of the other alkyl substituents (Table 11). Baker and Nathan[20] studied

TABLE 11

Compound	$Kx10^6$	Activation energy (kcal/mole)
$H_3C\!-\!C_6H_4CH_2Br$	83.5	18.9
$C_2H_5\!-\!C_6H_4CH_2Br$	62.6	19.4
$\begin{array}{c}H_3C\diagdown\\ \quad\ CH\!-\!C_6H_4CH_2Br\\ H_3C\diagup\end{array}$	46.95	19.8
$\begin{array}{c}H_3C\diagdown\\ \quad\ C\!-\!C_6H_4CH_2Br\\ H_3C\diagup\end{array}$	35.9	20.0
$C_6H_5CH_2Br$	2.85	21.0

[20] J. W. Baker and W. S. Nathan, *J. Chem. Soc.* p. 1844 (1935).

this reaction and developed the concept of hyperconjugation. One must note that the action of the substituents forms a series, which is the opposite of what one might expect on the basis of the induction effect. The polarizability of the CH_3 group is smaller than that of the isobutyl radical. Yet this would be important in the formation of the cation

$$R\text{---}C_6H_4CH_2^+$$

in the activated complex of the transition state. In contrast to this, a scheme can be written which indicates the electron distribution shift on account of hyperconjugation:

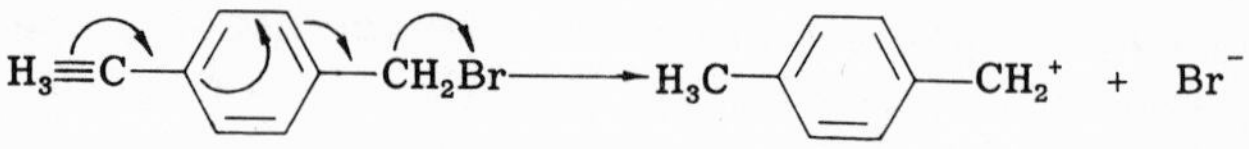

$$H_3\!\equiv\!C\text{---}\langle\!\bigcirc\!\rangle\text{---}CH_2Br\longrightarrow H_3C\text{---}\langle\!\bigcirc\!\rangle\text{---}CH_2^+ \ + \ Br^-$$

The dissociation of the negative bromide ion through the *p*-methyl group becomes quite plausible. A large number of reaction rates[21] show in analogous fashion the particular influence of the CH_3 group.

---

[21] E. D. Hughes, C. K. Ingold, and N. A. Taher, *J. Chem. Soc.* p. 949 (1940); F. Seel, *Z. angew. Chem.* **60**, 300 (1948); **61**, 89 (1949); E. Berliner and F. J. Bondhus, *J. Am. Chem. Soc.* **68**, 2355 (1946); **70**, 854 (1948); H. P. Rothbaum, I. Ting, and P. W. Robertson, *J. Chem. Soc.* p. 980 (1948); J. L. Bolland, *Quart. Revs. (London)* **3**, 1 (1949); E. H. Farmer, *Trans. Faraday Soc.* **38**, 341, 348, 356 (1942).

CHAPTER 17

Dipole Moment and Constitution*

If the centers of gravity of positive and negative charge do not coincide within a molecule, it must possess electrical asymmetry; one says that it is polar. This formal description forms the basis for the fact that the charge cloud in certain compounds is distributed unevenly over the molecular framework. The degree of asymmetry is described by the value of the dipole moment, which is the product of charge displacement Δe and distance l. The shift in charge quanta is of the order of magnitude of the elementary charge of the electron, i.e., 10^{-10} esu. The distance over which the charge is shifted may amount to several Angstrom units. The dipole moments in chemical compounds are of the order of 10^{-18} esu. This unit has been termed one Debye (D).

In a diatomic molecule AB, the charge asymmetry is caused by a difference in electronegativity x_A and x_B of the two atoms. According to Mulliken[1] the electronegativity of an atom x_A is best described by the average value of the ionization potential I_A and electron affinity E_A:

$$\tfrac{1}{2}(I_A + E_A).$$

This expression is related with the electronegativity of atoms A and B as follows:

$$(I_A + E_A) - (I_B + E_B) = 5.56(x_A - x_B).$$

The definition given by Pauling,[2] where the square root of the resonance energy between covalent and ionic structure of the compound $\sqrt{\Delta_{AB}}$ is

* See also C. P. Smyth, "Dielectric Behavior and Structure." McGraw-Hill, New York, 1955.

[1] R. S. Mulliken, *J. Chem. Phys.* **2**, 782 (1934); **3**, 573 (1935).

[2] L. Pauling, *J. Am. Chem. Soc.* **54**, 3570 (1932); cf. W. Hückel's critical observations, *J. prakt. Chem.* [4] **5**, 107 (1957).

taken as a measure of electronegativity, leads to the same gradation as Mulliken's definition.

The electronegativities of a selected group of elements are shown in Table 12. The difference between the values of two atoms in the table

TABLE 12*
Electronegativity of Some Elements

H						
2.1						
Li	Be	B	C	N	O	F
1.0	1.5	2.0	2.5	3.0	3.5	4.0
Na	Mg	Al	Si	P	S	Cl
0.9	1.2	1.5	1.8	2.1	2.5	3.0
K	Ca	Sc	Ge	As	Se	Br
0.8	1.0	1.3	1.8	2.0	2.4	2.8
Rb	Sr	Y	Sn	Sb	Te	I
0.8	1.0	1.2	1.7	1.8	2.1	2.5
Cs	Ba	La	Pb	Bi	Po	At
0.7	0.9	1.1	1.6	1.8	2.0	2.2

gives the approximate dipole moment of the corresponding compound.

In order to relate the dipole moment, which is a molecular constant, with the macroscopically observable properties of compounds, some mathematical derivations are necessary. The Clausius-Mosotti relation is a starting point, which may be derived without any reference to molecular concepts.

If a dielectric is contained between two parallel plates of a charged condenser, a small volume element contained in it has a field strength E_{in} and is related to the applied field strength E through the expression[3]

$$E_{in} = E + \frac{4\pi}{3} P. \tag{55a}$$

The dielectric polarization P is equal to the dipole moment induced in the volume element and must be proportional to the field strength E_{in} at each point:

$$P = n\bar{\alpha}E_{in} \tag{55b}$$

---

* Values are partly due to W. Gordy and W. J. Orville-Thomas, *J. of Chem. Phys.* **24,** 439 (1956).

[3] P. Debye, "Polar Molecules," p. 11. Dover Publs., New York, 1945.

where $\bar{\alpha}$ is the average polarizability of the molecules and n is the number of molecules per cubic centimeter. From Eqs. (55a) and (55b) one finds:

$$P(1 - \tfrac{4}{3}\pi n\bar{\alpha}) = n\bar{\alpha}E.$$

On the other hand, if a dielectric is interposed between the condenser plates, the specific surface charge σ is decreased. This decrease is ascribed to the induced dipole moment P of the dielectric per volume unit and has the dimension [charge · length/volume]. It can be considered as specific surface charge [charge/area] of the plates bordering the dielectric. The ratio of the two charge densities σ_v and $\sigma_v - P$ may be defined as the dielectric constant ϵ:

$$\epsilon = \frac{\sigma_v}{\sigma_v - P}. \tag{55c}$$

It had been derived that

$$\frac{\epsilon - 1}{\epsilon + 2} = \frac{4\pi}{3} n\bar{\alpha}.$$

If this expression is multiplied with the molar volume M/d where nM/d is equal to Avogadro's number N, one obtains the Clausius-Mosotti equation for molar polarization P_M:

$$P_M = \frac{\epsilon - 1}{\epsilon + 2} \cdot \frac{M}{d} = \frac{4\pi}{3} N\bar{\alpha}. \tag{55d}$$

Debye (1912) was able to prove that the molar polarization P_M is the contribution of two different kinds of polarization: one is the inductive contribution, and the other the orientation contribution. The former kind of polarization is caused by dipoles upon applying an electric field. The second is caused by orientation of already present permanent dipoles in the direction of the applied field. Chemical compounds therefore may be classified into two principal categories. The nonpolar group comprises compounds where dipole moments are caused only by induction. The second category of polar compounds, aside from this inductive dipole moment, must also have a permanent one. This permanent dipole moment is independent of any outside electric field. The inductive portion is identical with polarization, as expressed by the Clausius-Mosotti equation, i.e., $\tfrac{4}{3}\pi N\bar{\alpha}$. For the polar compounds, Debye was able to show that the antagonism between the orientation of dipoles in the electric field and their random orientation caused by heat is quantitatively described by the Boltzmann e-law. According to it, the orientation contribution is $\mu^2/3kT$, where μ is the permanent dipole moment, k is the Boltzmann constant, and T is the absolute temperature. The observed total polarization P_M is written in the Debye equation as follows:

$$P_M = \frac{\epsilon - 1}{\epsilon + 2} \cdot \frac{M}{d} = \frac{4}{3}\pi N \left(\alpha + \frac{\mu^2}{3kT} \right). \tag{56}$$

In order to arrive at the permanent dipole moment μ from the measured dielectric constant ϵ and the specific gravity d, the inductive contribution, $\frac{4}{3}\pi N\alpha$, must be subtracted. Several methods have been proposed. The most important are the measurement of molar polarization, and the determination of the temperature dependence of the total polarization. In the first method, one determines the term $\frac{4}{3}\pi N\alpha$ directly, which is identical with the molar refraction,

$$R = \frac{n^2 - 1}{n^2 + 2} \cdot \frac{M}{d} = \frac{4}{3}\pi N\overline{\alpha}, \tag{57}$$

and subtracts it from the value of the total polarization. It is necessary, however, to extrapolate to infinitely long wavelengths, because molar refraction is equal to electrostatic polarizability only at zero frequency. The Maxwell relationship $n^2 = \epsilon$ is valid strictly only for infinitely long

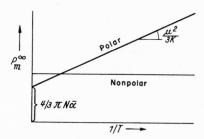

FIG. 20. Temperature dependence of molar polarization.

wavelengths. The second method is based on the determination of the total molar polarization as a function of temperature. The magnitude P_M is plotted against the reciprocal value of the absolute temperature, $1/T$. In the case of a permanent, temperature-independent dipole moment one obtains a straight line (Fig. 20). Its slope is equal to $\mu^2/3k$ from which the value of μ is determined. Compounds are dissolved in nonpolar solvents at varying concentrations, and the measured molar polarization is extrapolated to infinite dilution. This permits the elimination of dipole-dipole interaction.

Onsager[4] has tested the premises leading to the Debye equation (56) and has derived an expression for the polarization component

$$\frac{\epsilon - 1}{\epsilon + 2}\frac{M}{d} - \frac{\epsilon_\infty - 1}{\epsilon_\infty + 2}\frac{M}{d} = \frac{3\epsilon(\epsilon_\infty + 2)}{(2\epsilon + \epsilon_\infty)(\epsilon + 2)} \cdot \frac{4\pi N \mu^2}{9kT} \tag{57a}$$

where ϵ_∞ is the dielectric constant at very high frequencies where orientation of the dipoles can no longer take place.

The Onsager equation differs from the Debye equation by the factor

$$\frac{3\epsilon(\epsilon_\infty + 2)}{(2\epsilon + \epsilon_\infty)(\epsilon + 2)}$$

which becomes unity when $\epsilon = \epsilon_\infty$. Both equations then become identical, so that the Debye equation can be considered as a special case of the Onsager equation.

In order to understand the importance of the dipole moment in problems of chemical constitution, one must bear in mind that it is a vector quantity. It has magnitude as well as direction in space. The dipole moment is represented by an arrow, the direction of which conventionally points towards the center of gravity of the negative charge. Various charge rearrangements may take place at different positions in a molecule which may lead to partial moments. The total dipole moment is comprised not from the algebraic but the vector summation of these partial moments.

If one introduces a chlorine atom into the symmetrical and therefore nonpolar benzene molecule, one obtains monochlorobenzene C_6H_5Cl, which has a permanent dipole moment of 1.56 D. Since the chlorine is more electronegative than the phenyl ring, the vector arrow points in the direction of the chlorine:

1.56 D

If a second chlorine atom is introduced, three isomers, o-, m-, and p-dichlorobenzene, $C_6H_4Cl_2$, result with moments of 2.25, 1.48, and 0.0 D (I, II, and III). The values are derived from the parallelogram law for addition of partial moments of 1.56 D (μ-value of monochlorobenzene).

---

[4] L. Onsager, J. Am. Chem. Soc. **58**, 1486 (1936).

2. 25 D   1.48 D   0.0 D

(I)   (II)   (III)

Since the angle which the vector arrows form with each other increases in going from *ortho* through *meta* to the *para* compound, the total moment must decrease. In the *para* compound the two partial moments are equal and opposite so that a total moment of 0 results. The value of the dipole moment for proof of constitution is obvious. The example shows, in addition, that a total moment of 0 does not mean a completely nonpolar molecule. There may be strong partial moments which however, as in the case of *p*-dichlorobenzene, are intramolecularly compensated and cancel out. In certain reactions and molecular collisions these partial moments may assume considerable importance.

In the case of the *o*-, *m*-, and *p*-isomers of aminobenzoic acid one observes an increase of the permanent dipole moment from 1.0 for the *o*-, to 2.4 for the *m*-, and 3.3 for the *p*- compound. The vector addition of the partial moments of the NH_2 and COOH groups leads to these gradations. One must bear in mind that the partial moments of NH_2 and COOH groups are opposite in direction. Since the NH_2 group is more positive than the phenyl ring, the dipole vector points in the direction of the ring. On the other hand, the dipole vector of the carboxylic acid group points from the phenyl ring to the carboxyl group. Both vectors are additive in the *p*-position so that the total moment of this isomer reaches the maximum value of 3.3×10^{-18} esu (IV, V, VI).

1.0 D   2.4 D   3.3 D

(IV)   (V)   (VI)

The inductive shift of a common electron pair in favor of one of the bond partners can be studied in comparing the values of the dipole moments of alkyl halides. This kind of electron shift, which is based on the different electronegativity of the substituents, is called the induction effect. The dipole moments increase from methyl halide, 1.83 D, with increasing length of a paraffin chain (C_2H_5Cl, 2.0; C_3H_7Cl, 2.13) and approach a constant limiting value of 2.2×10^{-18} esu which no longer changes with increasing chain length. The explanation for this effect is that the electron pair between the halogen and the carbon is moved towards the former, on account of the greater electronegativity of the halogen. The charge asymmetry is propagated inductively for the higher alkyl derivatives through the chain, causing the dipole moment to increase with increasing chain length. The effect of the halogen slowly fades as the chain length increases, and the dipole moment then reaches a limiting value.

The inductive effect is characterized by the symbol $-I$ or $+I$, respectively, depending on the direction of the shift of the electrons in the hydrocarbon radical. It is written with a straight arrow in the direction of the electron shift: $CH_3 \rightarrow Cl$.

If one compares the dipole moment of simple benzene derivatives with those in the aliphatic series (Table 13) one notes differences which must be explained by different electron shift effects.

TABLE 13
Dipole Moments of Alkyl- and Aryl-Derivatives (in D)

	CH_3	C_6H_5
F	1.81	1.57
Cl	1.86	1.57
Br	1.82	1.55
CN	4.00	4.39
NO_2	3.5	4.19

The dipole moments of the alkyl halides are larger than those of the corresponding phenyl derivatives, whereas in the CN and NO_2 compounds the gradation is reversed. Here a second effect counteracts the induction effect which is based on the exchange interaction of the lone electron pairs of the substituent with the π electrons of the phenyl radical. This type of electron shift is termed the mesomeric effect[5] and is signified by $-M$ or $+M$, respectively, depending on whether the electron shift takes place from the phenyl ring to the substituent, or in the reverse direction. It is symbolized with a bent arrow in the direction of the electron shift. In the

[5] C. K. Ingold, "Structure and Mechanism in Organic Chemistry," p. 64. Cornell Univ. Press, Ithaca, N.Y., 1953.

aryl halides the mesomeric electronic shift is in favor of the phenyl radical $(+M)$ and counteracts the inductive effect $(-I)$. The dipole moments of the aryl halides therefore are smaller than those of the alkyl halides.

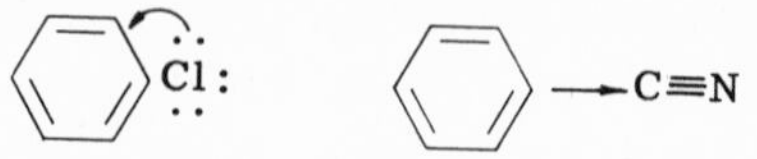

In the nitriles and the nitro compounds, the electron distribution between the π electrons of the double bonds and those of the phenyl ring are in the reverse direction $(-M)$. The mesomeric effect is added to the inductive effect, so that the dipole moment of the aryl derivatives is larger than that of the alkyl derivatives.

The marked difference between the two types of electron shift lies in the fact that in the inductive effect the electron pair is still common to the two bond partners. In contrast, in the mesomeric effect, owing to the distribution of the π electrons and the lone electron, a delocalization and migration of electric charge takes place through the whole molecule. The following example may demonstrate[6] this electron shift along the total skeleton of the molecule owing to the conjugated double bonds. In p-aminobenzoic acid ester, the movement of the free electron pair on the nitrogen extends along the phenyl radical towards the gaps in the oxygen sextet:

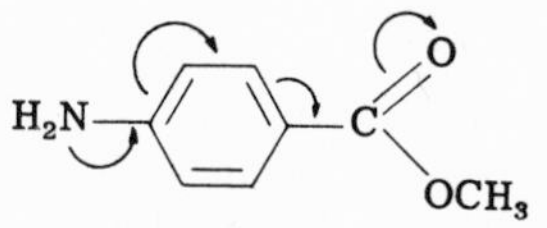

The small values for vinylamine, $CH_2\!=\!CH\!-\!NH_2$, and vinyl bromide, $CH_2\!=\!CHBr$, indicate the extent of the electron shift along the total molecule. Although these molecules are quite asymmetrical, the charge distribution is by and large symmetrical because the lone electrons in the NH_2 or bromine substituents, respectively, overlap with the π electrons of the neighboring double bond in a mesomeric manner, resulting in equalization of the polarity. The following gradation in dipole moments is found: C_2H_5Br 2.02, $CH_2\!=\!CH\!-\!Br$ 1.41, $CH\!\equiv\!CBr$ 0.0. The phenyl bromide molecule with a value of 1.71 lies between the value of a single and double bond, which agrees well with the bond character of the C—C bond in the benzene molecule (50% double bond character).

---

[6] T. M. Lowry, *J. Chem. Soc.* **123,** 822, 1886 (1923); *Nature* **114,** 376 (1925); C. K. Ingold and E. H. Ingold, *J. Chem. Soc.* p. 1310 (1926).

If one studies the gradations of dipole moments, one can find even more sophisticated differences in the electron shifts. The change of the dipole moment in the aliphatic nitrile and nitro compounds with increasing chain length is quite weak, going from 3.45 D to a constant limiting value of 3.70 D. The reason for this lies in the relatively high value of the dipole moment of the first member of the series, CH_3NO_2 (3.54 D). Hyperconjugation of the CH_3 group with double and triple bonds leads to a spreading of the electron distribution. This results in electrical asymmetry and electrical polarity which is measured as dipole moment. The increase of the dipole length by extending the chain must have very little influence under these circumstances.

The effect of hyperconjugation may be followed in studying dipole moment data in a series of hydrocarbons which have small but yet discrete permanent dipole moments (Table 14).

TABLE 14

Compound	Dipole moment (D)
$CH_3-CH=CH_2$	0.35
CH_3 $\diagdown$ $CH=CH_2$ $\diagup$ CH_3	0.30
$CH_3-C\equiv CH$	0.75
$CH_3-\langle\!\!\bigcirc\!\!\rangle$ 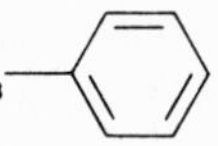	0.37
$CH_3-CH_2-CH_2-CH_2=CH_2$	0.51
$CH_3-CH=CH-CH_3$	0.00

Planarity of the molecule is a necessary prerequisite for the mesomeric effect $(\pm M)$. Otherwise there could be no distribution of the π electrons over the system of conjugated double bonds. The p-nitroaniline molecule has a large dipole moment (6.2 D) which exceeds the value obtained by vector addition of the partial dipole moment of the NH_2 and NO_2 groups (calculated to be 4.18 D). The combination of the NH_2 and NO_2 groups in the p-position results in an additional electron shift which can be written, based on mesomeric exchange, as follows:

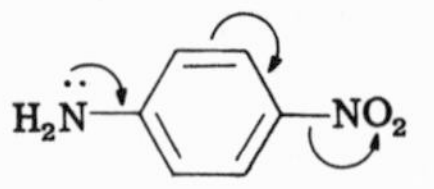

$$H_2N-\langle\rangle-NO_2$$

The two lone electrons in the NH_2 group move along the "conducting" phenyl ring to the gap in the oxygen atoms of the NO_2 group which act as acceptors. This shift increases the polarity of the molecule. However if one introduces voluminous CH_3 groups in the o-positions, the NO_2 and NH_2 groups are twisted out of the plane of the phenyl ring, and coplanarity of the molecule no longer exists. A mesomeric electronic shift can no longer take place and the dipole moment of 2,3,5,6-tetramethylnitroaniline

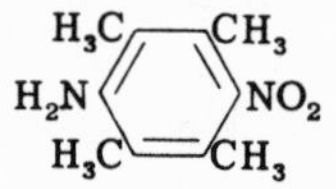

$$H_2N\langle\begin{smallmatrix}H_3C \quad CH_3 \\ \quad \\ H_3C \quad CH_3\end{smallmatrix}\rangle NO_2$$

falls back to the value 4.18 D in agreement with the value calculated by vector addition.

An experimental contribution to the connection between dipole moment and coplanarity of the molecule is furnished by measuring the dipole moments of the three triaryl methyl radicals.[7] The free radicals obtained in the equation

$$(C_6H_5)_3C-C(C_6H_5)_3 \rightleftharpoons 2\,(C_6H_5)_3C-$$

by dissociation of hexaphenylethane, as well as the monomeric tribiphenylmethyl have no permanent dipole moment in benzene solution. This finding

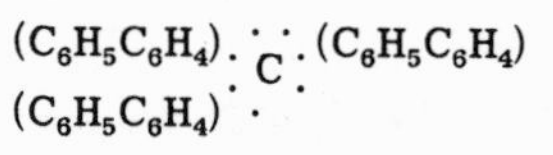

$$(C_6H_5C_6H_4)\cdot\overset{.}{\underset{.}{C}}\cdot(C_6H_5C_6H_4)$$
$$(C_6H_5C_6H_4)\cdot$$

must be explained in that the lone electron is no longer localized at the carbon atom but is spread out in its interaction with the π electrons of the phenyl groups over the total molecule. This extension goes hand in hand with planarity of the radical molecule which surrenders its tetrahedral symmetry in favor of a planar trigonal array.[8] Theilacker[9] succeeded in

[7] G. Karagounis and T. Jannakopoulos, Z. physik. Chem. **B47**, 343 (1940).

[8] E. Hückel, Z. Physik **83**, 632 (1933); Z. Elektrochem. **43**, 752 (1937); L. Pauling and G. W. Wheland, J. Chem. Phys. **1**, 362 (1933); **2**, 482 (1934).

[9] W. Theilacker and M. L. Wessel-Ewald, Ann. **594**, 214 (1955); W. Theilacker, B. Jung, and W. Rohde, ibid. p. 225 (1955).

synthesizing o-substituted triarylmethyl derivatives in the form of free radicals, which on sterical grounds could no longer have a planar structure. The problem concerning the cleavage of hexaarylethane into free radicals, where impedance towards formation of ethane on account of the space requirements of the substituents must be taken into account, does not seem to be answered as yet.[10]

A further use of dipole moments in explaining the charge distribution in the molecule is found in the term "per cent ionic character" of a bond. If one calculates the dipole moment of an ion pair from ionic charge and distance such as HCl or KCl in the vapor state, one obtains values of 6.14 D for HCl and 13.4 D for KCl. They are markedly different from the experimentally determined ones (1.0 D and 8.0 D). The calculation presupposes that ions are rigid spheres, and that approaching of oppositely charged ions does not change their contour. This, however, is not the case because of the polarizability of the ions. Both kinds of ions induce a polarity in the bonding partners which tends to decrease the calculated dipole moment. Fajans and Pauling proposed that the transition from the ionic towards the covalent bond takes place continuously. The mutual polarization changes the bond character which is mirrored in the value of the dipole moment. In the case of the ideal homopolar bond of the H_2 molecule, we have seen the case of strong mutual polarization of the H atoms leading to covalent bond formation. This polarization could be calculated by wave mechanical methods.

According to a proposal by Pauling, the difference between measured dipole moment and the calculated value based on assumption of rigid ions, permits a statement about the per cent electrovalent character, also referred to as per cent ionic character (see Table 15). One should note that the gradation in dipole moment would be in reverse series if the ions were not polarizable.

While the variation of the dipole moment with chemical structure has been treated using the MO method, it can also be explained using the VB theory. Instead of assuming a shift of the charge cloud because of the influence of substituents, one must stipulate that polar structures exist, which participate in the mesomeric state with corresponding coefficients. For example, the lesser dipole moment of chlorobenzene, in comparison with methyl chloride, is explained by the presence of a polar structure

---

[10] K. Ziegler, Z. angew. Chem. **61,** 168 (1949); for further views, see G. Karagounis, Helv. Chim. Acta **32,** 1840 (1949); **34,** 995 (1951).

TABLE 15
Dipole Moment and Covalent Character

Compound	Dipole moment, measured	Dipole moment, calculated	Per cent electrovalent character
CsI	11.0	17.8	62
CsCl	10.0	16.8	68
KCl	8.0	12.8	60
NaI	4.9	6.7	35
HF	1.91	2.7	43
HCl	1.08	1.2	17
HBr	0.80	0.89	11
HI	0.38	0.4	5

which has a dipole moment in the opposite direction of the nonpolar formula. This supports the observed decrease.

The quantum mechanical treatment[11] of the polarization phenomena leads to an equation which differs from the Debye equation in the permanent portion with a factor of $1 - f(T)$. Here, $f(T)$ is a temperature function in which the quantum h, the components of the dipole moments in the three directions in space, and the moments of inertia of the molecule are present as constants. On account of the large moment of inertia of the dipoles, this factor numerically is of little consequence. However, for molecules with a small momentum of inertia, such as HF, the difference between classical and wave mechanical calculations amounts to 0.03 D.

The Debye method for the calculation of the dipole moment from measured molar polarization data presupposes that the polar molecules are dissolved in a nonpolar environment, and that the polarization values are extrapolated to infinite dilution in order to eliminate the influence of local fields.

A great number of substances such as amino acids and others are only

[11] J. H. Van Vleck, "The Theory of Electric and Magnetic Susceptibilities." Oxford Univ. Press, London and New York, 1932.

soluble in polar solvents. For this class of compounds Kirkwood[12] developed a theory which accounts for the presence of a special inner electric field. This method permits one to calculate the dipole moment from the molar polarization in polar solvents for the dissolved substance. As one may expect, very high values of dipole moments are found in the case of amino acids on account of their zwitterion character. These values increase proportionally with the square root of the number of carbon atoms (cf. Table 16).

TABLE 16
Dipole Moments of Some Amino Acids

Compound	D ($\times 10^{-18}$ esu)
Glycine	15.5
β-Alanine	19.0
Aminocaproic acid	28.0
Hexaglycine	50.0
Albumin	250–1500

Recently it has been possible to determine dipole moments very accurately with the use of microwave spectroscopy. The method consists of the determination of the absorption coefficient of substances in the wavelength range 1.5–3 cm which corresponds energetically to the changes of the rotation states of the molecule. It permits one to determine the dipole moment of a substance from the intensity of the pure rotation spectrum in this wavelength range, or from the line splitting in the electrical field (Stark effect). Depending on the rotation quantum number, the rotation states are degenerate by the amount $(2I + 1)$, because the energy state of the rotating molecule can be constructed from the rotation quantum number I to $2I + 1$. If one applies an electric field, the equality of the energy states is partially disturbed and the degeneracy removed. The energy differences ΔE resulting from this splitting are represented by:

$$\Delta E = \left(\frac{2\pi\mu\mathfrak{E}}{h}\right)^2 In \left(\frac{I(I + 1) - 3M^2}{I(I + 1)(2I - 1)(2I + 3)}\right) \qquad (57b)$$

where $\mathfrak{E}$ is the electric field strength, In is the moment of inertia (in the case of a linear molecule), μ is the dipole moment, and M is the magnetic quantum number.

---

[12] J. G. Kirkwood, in "Proteins, Amino Acids, and Peptides" (E. J. Cohn and J. T. Edsall, eds.), p. 276. Reinhold, New York, 1943.

Table 17 shows a series of dipole moments which have been determined by this method. The accuracy of this new technique is evident from the three decimal positions, which is important particularly for molecules with small dipole moments.

TABLE 17

Dipole Moments Using the Stark Effect in the Microwave Region

Compound	Dipole moment	Compound	Dipole moment
COS	0.710 ± 0.004	CHF_3	1.645×0.009
N_2O	0.166 ± 0.002	CH_3Cl	1.869 ± 0.010
H_2O	1.94 ± 0.06	NH_3	1.468 ± 0.009
D_2O	$1.87 \pm 1\%$	PH_3	0.55 ± 0.01
O_3	0.53 ± 0.02	AsH_3	0.22 ± 0.02
HNCO	1.592 ± 0.010	SbH_3	0.116 ± 0.002
BrCl	0.57 ± 0.02	HN_3	0.847 ± 0.05
CH_2O	2.339 ± 0.013	B_5H_9	2.13 ± 0.04
CH_3OH	0.895	$CH_3C\equiv CH$	0.75 ± 0.001

CHAPTER 18

Molar Refraction, Magnetic
Susceptibility, and the
Chemical Bond

Electric displacement polarization is measured by extrapolating molar refraction to infinite wavelengths. It has been most useful in the electronic theory of organic compounds in its application to chemical constitution problems. The molar refraction is a characteristic constant describing the electronic state of the molecule. It indicates the induced dipole moment if an external electric field is applied and therefore is a measure of the mobility of electric charges within the molecule. The relationship can be shown in the following equation:

$$R = \frac{n^2 - 1}{n^2 + 2} \cdot \frac{M}{d} = \frac{4}{3} \pi N \bar{\alpha} = \frac{4}{3} \pi N \frac{\mu_{ind}}{\mathfrak{E}}, \tag{58}$$

where $\bar{\alpha}$ is the average polarizability of the molecule, $\mathfrak{E}$ is the unit of field strength, and μ_{ind} is the induced dipole moment in the three directions of space. Any permanent dipole moment which may be present is not measured in the molar refraction. This is based on the fact that permanent dipoles, owing to their inertia, are not oriented in the high frequency field of visible light. However, the electrons follow the rapid field change of the electric light vector which causes the creation of an induced dipole moment. Yet even electrons possess inertia, and if the field changes rapidly, a certain time lag results shown by the dependence of the refraction values from wavelength. If one wishes to reach the static case of an electric field at rest, i.e., the theoretically ideal state of reference, one must determine molar refraction for several frequencies and extrapolate to zero frequency.

A great number of investigations in the past century (Landolt, Brühl, Eisenlohr) aimed to separate the molar refraction into atomic refraction values. The objective was to calculate molar refraction from atomic refraction values and obtain inside information about the constitution of unknown molecules. It became apparent that double bonds, triple bonds, and ring systems with different ring size must have their own refraction values which have been termed increments. Table 18 summarizes a number of atomic refraction values and increments.

TABLE 18

Atomic Refractions and Bond Increments

H	1.100	C=C increment	1.733
$O_{(alcohol)}$	1.525	C≡C increment	2.398
$O_{(ether)}$	1.643	F	1.090
$O_{(carboxyl)}$	2.211	F^-	2.5
C	2.418	Cl	5.967
$N_{(RNH_2)}$	2.322	Cl^-	8.7
$N_{(R_2-NH)}$	2.499	Br	8.863
$N_{(R_3N)}$	2.840	Br^-	12.2

The usefulness of molar refraction as a tool for clarifying the constitution of chemical structures is quite limited owing to its great susceptibility towards the influence of constituents. For example, nitrogen, depending on the type of bond and the nature of the neighboring atom, has no less than 30 different values of atomic refraction. Following the Lewis theory of the covalent bond, the knowledge of the formation of octets, and the sharing of a common electron pair between partners, attempts were made to divide molar refraction into values of individual electronic octets (Steiger, Fajans, Knorr, Ruby, 1921–1928). The advantage of this type of representation lies in the larger number of variations. These possibilities leave room for the above-mentioned large number of atomic refraction values. In Table 19 some octet refraction values are summarized and examples for structures are reported in the third column.

One can see that the refraction of an electron octet around the C atom amounts to 6.80 cm^3/mol if it is bound to four H atoms. On the other hand, the value is only 4.84 cm^3/mol if the C atom shares its octet with four other C atoms. This is the same as stating that the mobility of electrons, i.e., the polarizability of a bond between an sp^3 hybrid and a 1s electron ($sp^3 - 1s$) is larger than between two sp^3 hybrids ($sp^3 - sp^3$). Since a 1s state has a spherical electron distribution, while an sp^3 hybrid has a vectorlike direction, this statement appears quite plausible. Saturation of two sp^3 hybrids leads to a concentric and hence less polarizable bond than one involving a

TABLE 19

Atom	Type of bond	Compound (as example)	Refraction value of the octet (cm^3/mole)
C	4 $(1s\text{-}sp^3)$	CH_4	6.80
C	4 $(sp^3\text{-}sp^3)$	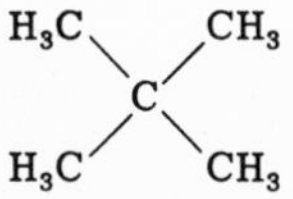 $H_3C\diagdown\diagup CH_3$ C $H_3C\diagup\diagdown CH_3$	4.84
O	2 $(1s\text{-}2p)$	H_2O	3.76
O	$(1s\text{-}2p)$ $(sp^3\text{-}2p)$	$H_3C{-}OH$	3.23
O	2 $(sp^3\text{-}2p)$	$H_3C{-}O{-}CH_3$	2.85
N	3 $(1s\text{-}2p)$	NH_3	5.65
N	2 $(1s\text{-}2p)$ $(sp^3\text{-}2p)$	$H_3C{-}NH_2$	5.13
N	$(1s\text{-}2p)$ 2 $(sp^3\text{-}2p)$	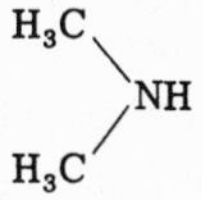 $H_3C\diagdown$ NH $H_3C\diagup$	4.81
N	3 $(sp^3\text{-}2p)$	$(CH_3)_3N$	4.65

$1s$ state. A methyl group has an octet which is polarized with greater ease than the tertiary butyl radical:

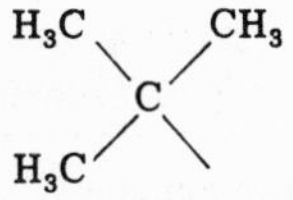

$$H_3C\diagdown\ \diagup CH_3$$
$$C$$
$$H_3C\diagup\ \diagdown$$

This demonstrates the donor properties of a CH_3 group which already had been encountered in the hyperconjugation effect (p. 90).

Similar considerations can be made regarding the change of the refraction value of ammonia (5.65 cm^3/mol) and water (3.76 cm^3/mol) by replacing the H atoms with a CH_3 group, resulting in a transition of a $2p$-$1s$ to a $2p$-sp^3 bond. The refraction values of the corresponding octets decrease from 4.65 cm^3/mol for trimethylamine to 2.85 cm^3/mol for methyl ether. As a good example for the mobility of the electrons as a measure of molar refraction in the atomic or molecular bond, one may compare the refraction values of the following isoelectronic compounds:

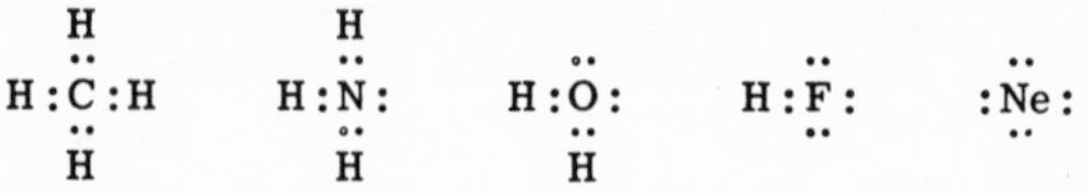

$$
\begin{array}{ccccc}
\text{H} & \text{H} & & & \\
\text{H:C:H} & \text{H:N:} & \text{H:O:} & \text{H:F:} & \text{:Ne:} \\
\text{H} & \text{H} & \text{H} & & \\
\\
6.80 & 5.65 & 3.76 & 1.9 & 1.00
\end{array}
$$

In this series the electronic octet is under the influence of the increasing nuclear charge number of the central atom. This influence serves to strengthen the electron octet from carbon to neon. The polarizability becomes smaller and the molar refraction decreases. The respective strengths of bonding of the electron octet to the central atom can also be noted from another property in this series: the ability of these compounds to dissociate H atoms as protons. This tendency rapidly increases from CH_4 to NH_3 to H_2O to HF.[1] HF is a strong acid while neon has no tendency whatever to accept H in any of its four lone electron pairs. On the other, hand, the more electronegative the central atom, the less the molar refraction of the octet.

The following examples illustrate that one must differentiate between the polarization state of a molecule expressed by its permanent dipole moment, and its polarizability, i.e., the possibility of its centers of electric charge being displaced. The more strongly a molecule is polarized, the smaller is its polarizability. This is readily seen in the series of hydrogen halides. Permanent and induced dipole moments move in opposite directions (see Table 20).

TABLE 20
Permanent and Induced Dipole Moments of Hydrogen Halides

Hydrogen halide	Dipole moment, permanent	Dipole moment, induced
HF	1.91	—
HCl	1.08	3.6
HBr	0.80	5.0
HI	0.38	7.6

[1] E. Wiberg, *Z. physik. Chem.* **A143,** 97 (1923).

The same explanation holds for the fact that among isomeric compounds, the one with the higher dipole moment has the smaller molar refraction.

A compound with conjugated double bonds falls in a special category from the point of view of polarizability. Additional parameters over and above the additive values of molar refraction have to be invoked. These values are larger than the refraction increments for the individual double bonds and are referred to as exaltation. They may be explained as a spreading out with a concomitant loosening of the electrons, which is a sequel of a planar system having conjugated double bonds. We can best study this effect by comparing the molar refraction of the aromatic and aliphatic series (see Table 21). There are indicated the difference of the atomic

TABLE 21

Comparison of the Atomic Refraction of Some Elements in
Aliphatic and Aromatic Compounds[a]

Compound pair		$(R_S)_{arom.} - (R_S)_{aliph.}$	S
$C_6H_5N(CH_3)_2$	$(CH_3)_3N$	1.41	N
$C_6H_5OCH_3$	CH_3OCH_3	0.54	O
C_6H_5SH	CH_3SH	0.49	S
C_6H_5I	CH_3I	0.18	I
$(C_6H_5)_2O$	$(CH_3)_2O$	1.20	O
$(C_5H_6)_3P$	$(CH_3)_3P$	3.47	P

[a] Values taken from C. K. Ingold, "Structure and Mechanism in Organic Chemistry" Cornell Univ. Press, Ithaca, N. Y., 1953.

refraction of the element S (fourth column) in aromatic and aliphatic compounds. One is led to conclude that the additivity of molar refraction no longer holds if the molecule has mesomeric properties. What had been termed exaltation in the molar refraction of organic compounds is nothing but an increase in the total polarizability, caused by the extension of the π electrons over the conjugated double bond system.

Analogous behavior is found in the magnetic properties of the molecule. The additivity of the magnetic molar constant (susceptibility) holds as long as electrons participating in a bond are localized in certain positions. Molecules with conjugated double bonds, however, show far-reaching deviations from additivity which must be explained as mesomeric electron shifts. In order to understand them, the relationship between macroscopic and molecular magnetic constants must be clarified, as was done in electronic molar polarization.

Faraday (1845) recognized that all matter can be magnetized. One differentiates between two types of matter, diamagnetic and paramagnetic depending on whether the corresponding substances are drawn into or expelled from an inhomogeneous magnetic field (Fig. 21). The action of a

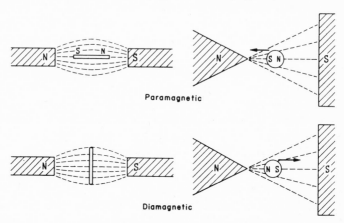

FIG. 21. Behavior of substances in a magnetic field.

homogeneous magnetic field is only directive; a diamagnetic rod orients itself perpendicularly, whereas a paramagnetic one assumes a parallel orientation to the magnetic lines of force. In an inhomogeneous magnetic field, aside from the above orientation, there is also a migration of the paramagnetic matter towards the domains of higher field strength. Diamagnetic matter, on the other hand, moves in the direction of lesser field strength. In order to explain the different behavior one must assume that the exterior magnetic field induces a magnetic dipole moment within the material. The magnetic poles of paramagnetic substances are opposed to the outer magnetic field. This produces migration towards lines of higher field strength. In diamagnetic matter, the influence of the induced magnetic moment has the opposite direction, i.e., repulsion, causing migration of the magnetized matter towards lines of lesser field strength.

The present-day concept of elementary circular currents can be used in a modified form to explain magnetic properties. The phenomenon of ferromagnetism, a limiting case of very strong paramagnetism, was explained by Ampère as the orientation of irregular, random-oriented, elementary currents through the exterior magnetic field. According to these concepts, paramagnetic matter contains permanent magnetic dipoles, resulting from uncompensated orbital moments or uncompensated spin moments of lone electrons. In the case of diamagnetic matter, however, magnetic moments are only created through induction by applying the exterior field. They result from a change in velocity of the rotating electron and are always opposed to the direction of the exterior field.

The connections can be shown schematically in Fig. 22. Two electron

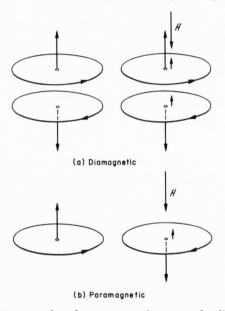

(a) Diamagnetic

(b) Paramagnetic

FIG. 22. Schematic representation of a paramagnetic atom and a diamagnetic molecule.

currents are coupled in a molecule so that their direction has an opposing sense (a). The magnetic moments are perpendicular to the circular orbital (indicated by an arrow) and opposed to each other so that the molecule has no permanent moment, because of compensation of the magnetic moments. If an exterior magnetic field of strength H is applied, the induction according to the Lenz' rule accelerates the orbital motion of the electron in the upper orbital and retards the one in the lower. In both cases these current intensity changes correspond to induced magnetic moments which are opposed to the exterior magnetic field; they reduce the action of the field (they are indicated by small arrows shown next to the longer arrows). The substance is said to be diamagnetic. The paramagnetic case is shown in scheme (b). Only one noncompensated circular current is present, which does not cause a magnetic moment. It is independent of the presence of an exterior magnetic field and belongs permanently to the molecule. If an external field is applied, the molecule is oriented in the direction of the field lines, which intensifies the action of the field. Simultaneously, the applied field induces, as stated above, an opposing sense in the circular orbital of the electron, so that an opposingly oriented magnetic moment results. This corresponds to the diamagnetic portion of the molecule which is present in all matter, including paramagnetic substances, as long as there are moving electrons.

If a coil carrying a current is introduced in a medium whose magnetic properties are to be studied, the magnetic field strength H_0 is changed by a positive or negative amount J depending on whether the substance is paramagnetic or diamagnetic. The effective magnetic field strength within a substance is expressed by

$$H_{\text{eff.}} = H_0 \pm J. \tag{59}$$

J denotes the induced magnetic dipole moment per cubic centimeter (pole strength $\times$ distance, $p \times l$) and is called magnetic polarization. It was found experimentally that the magnetic polarization J is proportional to the applied field strength H_0. The proportionality factor κ multiplied by 4π is a characteristic constant* for any substance which has magnetic susceptibility because it expresses the receptiveness of matter for the magnetic state. κ is a pure number and has no dimensions. It indicates the magnetizability of 1 cm³ of matter.[2] It is positive for paramagnetic and negative for diamagnetic matter, and its numerical values fall between 10^{-6} and 10^{-4}. The relationships can be summarized in the following equations:

$$J = \frac{p \cdot l}{cm^3} = 4\pi\kappa H_0 \tag{60}$$

$$H_{\text{eff.}} = H_0 + 4\pi\kappa H_0 = H_0(1 + 4\pi\kappa) \tag{61}$$

$$\frac{H_{\text{eff.}}}{H_0} = 1 + 4\pi\kappa = \mu. \tag{62}$$

The ratio of the effective magnetic field strength, $H_{\text{eff.}}$, to the original field strength, H_0, is called the magnetic permeability μ because it is a measure

---

* The factor 4π is used because 4π force lines are directed into space from the unit of magnetic field strength.

[2] For dimensions cf. P. W. Selwood, "Magnetochemistry," 2nd ed. Interscience, New York, 1956.

of the penetrability of the substance by magnetic force lines. For paramagnetic matter μ is larger than 1; for diamagnetic matter μ is smaller than 1, since κ is positive in the former and negative in the latter case. The density of field lines increases by immersing the coil in paramagnetic matter. In diamagnetic matter it decreases. The field lines are expelled from the substance.

The chemist does not make use of the value κ which refers to a cm³ but employs the molar susceptibility χ which is obtained by multiplying κ by the molar volume[3]:

$$\chi = \kappa \cdot \frac{M}{d}. \tag{63}$$

The manner in which the combination of atomic orbitals leads to paramagnetic or diamagnetic molecular orbitals, respectively, will be shown in the example of the formation of the oxygen or nitrogen molecule, respectively, from their corresponding atoms.

If two oxygen atoms A and A' approach each other from a large distance, the atomic orbitals fuse into molecular orbitals. The respective energy states are shown diagrammatically in Fig. 23. One notes that states of equal energy and equal symmetry of electron cloud distribution act upon each other ($\leftrightarrow$), and that by splitting a bonding and a antibonding (designated with asterisks) orbital a molecular orbital is formed. Each of these states is occupied at most with two electrons of opposing spin. Yet, according to Hund's rule, electrons prefer single positions over pairing. In the O_2 molecule there are eight electrons forming four bonding orbitals (the $\sigma 2s$, $\sigma 2p$, and the doubly degenerate $\pi_y 2p$, $\pi_z 2p$) and four electrons, occupying four antibonding orbitals ($\sigma^* 2s$, $\pi_y^* 2p$, $\pi_z^* 2p$). As a sequel there are four electrons accounting for attraction in the O=O bond if the fact that the antibonding terms are not exactly symmetrical to the bonding ones is disregarded. The sum of the energies of the two separated oxygen atoms is not shown in the diagram. The bond order in the O_2 molecule is 2. Its ground state is a triplet state $^3\Sigma_g$ because it contains two lone electrons ($\pi_y^* 2p$ and $\pi_z^* 2p$). These two electrons, on account of their spin moments, are responsible for the paramagnetism of the O_2 molecule.[4] In the nitrogen atom, which directly precedes oxygen in the periodic system, the $2p_z$ state

[3] See C. A. Hutchison, Jr., *in* "Determination of Organic Structures by Physical Methods" (E. A. Braude and F. C. Nachod, eds.), Vol. I, p. 259. Academic Press, New York, 1955.

[4] J. E. Lennard-Jones, *Trans. Faraday Soc.* **25,** 668 (1929).

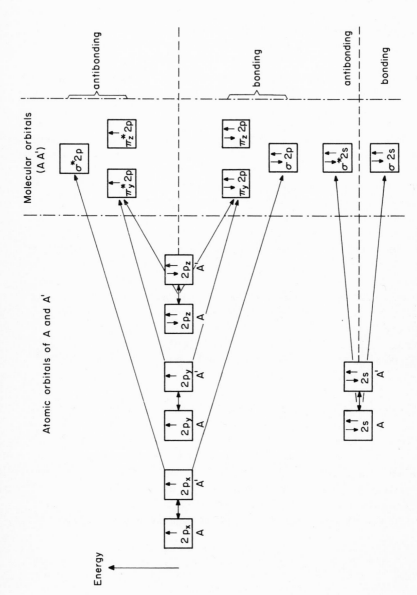

FIG. 23. Demonstration of paramagnetism of the O_2 molecule.

is only singly occupied. Using the same scheme for the formation of the N_2 molecules, the antibonding and doubly degenerate orbitals π_y^*2p and π_z^*2p remain unoccupied. Consequently, in the nitrogen molecule only electrons with paired compensated spins occur, so that the molecule is diamagnetic. The molecule is in the singlet state, $^1\Sigma_g$, and is held together with six electrons (eight bonding less two nonbonding). Its bond order is 3.

In an analogous fashion one can prove that the F_2 molecule is diamagnetic, because in contrast with the O_2 molecule, the additional two electrons complete the antibonding doubly degenerate orbitals π_y^*2p, π_z^*2p, and change the triplet state into a singlet state ($^1\Sigma_g$). Concomitantly, the number of the effectively bonding electrons is decreased to two (eight bonding less six nonbonding) which corresponds to the bond order of 1. These facts correspond with the magnetic behavior and the dissociation energies of the molecules N_2, O_2, F_2, and agree with their bond orders values of 7.4, 5.1, and 2.8 ev, respectively.

The extensive work of Pascal[4a] (1914) showed that the magnetic molar susceptibility χ of saturated organic compounds could be separated into atomic susceptibilities. Unknown molar susceptibilities could be calculated by simple addition of atomic susceptibilities. The presence of double and triple bonds required particular portions of magnetic susceptibility which again were termed increments. Table 22 contains the susceptibilities of

TABLE 22

Atomic Susceptibilities and Increments ($\times 10^6$)

H	-2.93	S	-15
C	-6.00	Se	-23
N	-5.55 (chain)	B	-7
N	-4.61 (ring)	Si	-13
N	-1.54 (RNH_2)	P	-10
N	-2.11 (R_2NH)	As	-21
O	-4.61 (ROH, ROR)	C=C	$+5.5$
O	$+1.72$ (Carbonyl)	C=C—C=C	$+10.6$
F	-6.3	N=N	$+1.85$
Cl	-20.1	C=N	$+8.15$
Br	-30.6	C≡N	$+0.8$
I	-44.6	C_6H_6	-1.4
		Cyclohexane	-3.0

[4a] P. Pascal, *Ann. chim. phys.* **19**, 5 (1910); **25**, 289 (1912); **29**, 218 (1913). Cf. S. S. Bhatnagar and K. M. Mathur, "Physical Principles and Applications of Magnetochemistry." Macmillan, London, 1935.

some atoms as well as increments for double and triple bonds. In studying these numbers one notes that the magnetic susceptibility of the atoms increases with increase in atomic radius. Indeed, Larmor and Langevin[5] derived the relationship:

$$\chi = \frac{Ne^2}{6c^2m} \sum \overline{r^2}, \tag{64}$$

based on the Bohr atomic model, which shows the connection between molar susceptibility and the sum of the mean squares of all orbital radii r occurring in the molecule. In this equation m and e are the mass and charge of an electron, N is Avogadro's number, and c is the velocity of light.

The dependence on the radius is most pronounced if one compares the susceptibilities of isoelectronic atoms or ions respectively. With increasing positive nuclear charge, the value of susceptibility decreases, which is related to a smaller atomic radius and to the contracting action of the positive charge.

In the same manner, based on the electron distribution of different types of bonds (cf. Chapter 15), the positive increments of double and triple bonds can be explained. One might be tempted to explain these increments as paramagnetic contributions of free π electrons of the double and triple bonds. However, this explanation is not correct. It will be seen below, in the case of free radicals, that such contributions, if they should be present, must be of a completely different order of magnitude. Rather, one does not deal here with the occurrence of paramagnetism, but with a decrease in diamagnetism. If one replaces an sp^3 hybrid bond with an axial symmetrical distribution of the electron cloud along the C—C line with a π bond, the circulation radius of an electron (radius of its residence probability) is decreased, since in the same connecting line a nodal plane occurs which separates the charge cloud into two halves. The diamagnetic susceptibility therefore must decrease in going from a single to a double bond, which appears as a positive increment since κ is negative for diamagnetism. If one further replaces an sp^2 hybrid by a second π bond (changing from double to triple bond), a second π cloud perpendicular to the first is formed. The circulation radius is increased over the double bond and the corresponding decrease in diamagnetism is lessened.

---

[5] Cf. J. H. Van Vleck, "The Theory of Electric and Magnetic Susceptibilities," p. 206. Oxford Univ. Press, London and New York, 1932; also P. W. Selwood, "Magneto-chemistry," p. 33. Interscience, New York, 1953.

The additional values of magnetic susceptibility which occur in conjugated double bonds must be explained in the same fashion. As we have stressed before, conjugation causes a delocalization of electrons, so that the π electrons in essence are freely moving along the skeleton of σ bonds. They have a larger magnetic radius and hence produce an increase in diamagnetism. Thus one can explain that while the diamagnetic susceptibility of two conjugated double bonds is only 0.5 units larger than the sum of the individual susceptibilities, compounds with typical aromatic character such as benzene, pyridine, thiophene, etc., show an increase of eighteen full units. Furthermore, if two benzene rings combine into a diphenyl molecule, an additional increase of 0.5 units over the 18 units per phenyl radical is noted, which is based on the resonance of the π electrons of the two phenyl rings. If one increases the radius of the electrons in the sense of the Larmor-Langevin equation (64) in going to condensed ring systems such as naphthalene, anthracene, chrysene, etc., the extra values of diamagnetism, termed exaltations, increase. The spreading of the delocalized electrons can also extend to substituents such as Cl, Br, and I, acting like a side-chain. This is evident in the increase of diamagnetic susceptibility in the above series of the halogens.

The investigations of Raman and Krishnan,[6] on the one hand, and of Lonsdale,[7] on the other, into the diamagnetism of single crystals of organic compounds have been revealing in that they permit one to make a statement about the susceptibility in the various axial directions within the molecule. One can follow step by step the increase of the action of the π electrons with increasing number of phenyl rings, if one subtracts from the portion of the measured magnetic susceptibility the amount which corresponds to the σ bonds.[8] While this portion remains constant for all ring systems, independent of the number of rings, and corresponds numerically to the value for diamond ($\chi = 6.0 \times 10^{-6}$), the portion of the diamagnetism resulting from the π electrons increases with increasing number of rings. In graphite, the susceptibility as well as the conjugation approach a maximum value with a magnetic radius of 7.8 Å. Table 23 shows the magnetic susceptibility of the series of planar molecules. It gives average values of the magnetic susceptibility in two parallel directions within the molecular plane $(\chi_x + \chi_y)/2$ and the magnetic susceptibility in the direction of the

[6] C. V. Raman and K. S. Krishnan, *Proc. Roy. Soc.* **A113,** 511 (1927).

[7] K. Lonsdale, *Proc. Roy. Soc.* **A159,** 149 (1937).

[8] L. Pauling, *J. Chem. Phys.* **4,** 673 (1936).

z-axis, i.e., perpendicular to the plane of the molecule. The latter is the difference between the average total susceptibility $\bar{\chi}$ and the average value $\frac{1}{2}(\chi_x + \chi_y)$. Since the residence probability of the π electrons in the plane of benzene is small, one ascribes the magnetic susceptibilities χ_x and χ_y to the σ electrons. After subtracting these values from the total susceptibility, the π electrons remain. Table 23 summarizes the calculated radii

TABLE 23

Molar Susceptibilities and Molar Radii

Compound	σ electrons[a]	r_σ	π electrons[b]	r_π
Benzene	37.3	0.74	54.0	1.46
Biphenyl	63.4	0.70	118.6	1.53
Triphenyl	92.5	0.70	178	1.52
Naphthalene	55.0	0.71	114.0	1.64
Anthracene	60.2	0.69	182.6	1.75
Phenanthrene	74.0	0.71	166	1.67
Chrysene	85.7	0.68	225.2	1.72
Pyrene	80.6	0.70	232	1.82
Graphite	6.0	0.81	258	7.80

[a] $\frac{1}{2}(\chi_x + \chi_y) \times 10^6$.

[b] $(\bar{\chi} - \frac{1}{2}(\chi_x + \chi_y)) \times 10^6$.

based on the assumptions of the Langevin equation for the probable residence of σ and π electrons.

Relatively few compounds exist which are paramagnetic. Aside from O_2, SO_2, and NO, there are the organic free radicals with lone, uncompensated electrons which possess a permanent magnetic moment, the determination of which is carried out according to methods which are similar to the determination of the electric dipole moment. The measured total molar susceptibility χ is the sum of the always present diamagnetic susceptibility, χ_d, and the possibly occurring paramagnetism, χ_p. The latter property is temperature-dependent, since the orientation of permanent dipoles in the magnetic field opposes the thermal motion. They are combined in the following relationship:[9]

$$\chi = \chi_{dia} + \chi_{para} = \chi_{dia} + \frac{N^2\mu^2}{3RT}. \tag{65}$$

If one determines χ at various temperatures and plots the values against $1/T$, one obtains a straight line with slope $N^2\mu^2/3RT$. N again is Avogadro's

[9] P. Langevin, *J. Phys.* **4,** 678 (1905); *Ann. chim. phys.* **5,** 70 (1905).

number, R is the gas constant, and μ is the measured magnetic dipole moment. One can obtain the value of the permanent magnetic moment also by a second method: one calculates the diamagnetic contribution χ_d from the atomic susceptibility, and then subtracts this value from the total molar magnetizability. According to quantum theory the magnetic moment of a compound $(p \times l)$ cannot assume any value, but must be a whole multiple of the Bohr magneton β. The Bohr magneton is described by the expression

$$\beta = \frac{h \cdot e}{4\pi m}. \tag{66}$$

This is the smallest magnetic moment which results from the circular current of the narrowest orbital radius of the H atom for a moving electron. Its value is equal to 0.917×10^{-20} erg/gauss. This value has the property of an elementary quantum which is no further divisible. All real occurring values of magnetic dipoles are higher than this quantity. In the case of magnetic spin moments they are expressed by $\sqrt{4S(S + 1)}$ where S is the sum of the spin quantum numbers of all unpaired electrons within the compound. A free radical, for example, "trivalent carbon," which has a single unpaired electron, has a magnetic moment of $\sqrt{3}\beta = 1.73\beta$ or 1.73 Bohr magnetons.

Investigations by E. Müller and Müller-Rodloff[10] indicated that presence of paramagnetism in organic compounds with the value of 1.73 Bohr magnetons is the most certain criterion for the appearance of free radicals, if the electron has no orbital momentum ($^2\Sigma_{\frac{1}{2}}$-term). In former times, the characteristic for the presence of free radicals with a long lifetime was believed to have been the intensive absorption in the visible light range, which did not obey Beer's law, and a strong susceptibility towards oxygen. These criteria do not hold in compounds which are completely dissociated. The fact that this criterion is quite uncertain for certain classes of compounds can be shown in the hydrocarbon of Tschitschibabin which can be written as two formulas, a quinoid (I), and a biradical (II) structure.

$(C_6H_5)_2C = \langle \text{ring} \rangle = \langle \text{ring} \rangle = C(C_6H_5)_2;$ $(C_6H_5)_2C \langle \text{ring} \rangle - \langle \text{ring} \rangle - C(C_6H_5)_2.$

(I)   (II)

[10] E. Müller and I. Müller-Rodloff, *Ann.* **520**, 235; **521**, 81 and 89 (1935); N. W. Taylor, *J. Am. Chem. Soc.* **48**, 854 (1926).

On the basis of chemical properties no definite selection in favor of one can be made. Magnetic measurements indicate that the compound is diamagnetic and argue in favor of the quinoid structure (I). On the other hand, one knows compounds which are intensively colored and easily oxidizable such as the blue pentacene

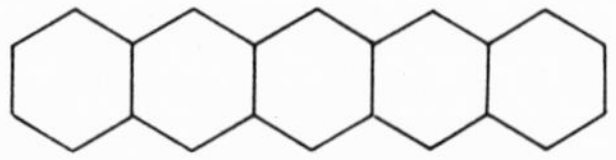

and tetraphenylnaphthacene

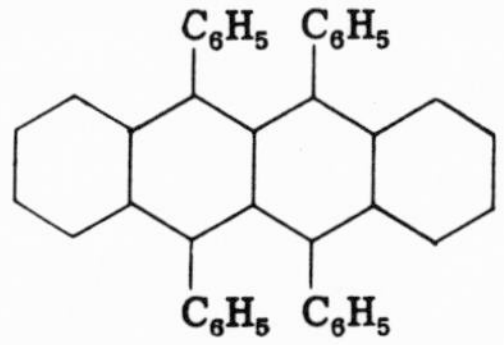

which are not free radicals, in agreement with the fact that they are diamagnetic.

The change of paramagnetism upon dilution of hexaphenylethane solutions permits one to determine the degree of dissociation of this compound into the free radical triphenylmethyl. The radical tribiphenylmethyl $(C_6H_5C_6H_4)_3C\cdot$ shows paramagnetism even in the solid state with 1.73 Bohr magnetons and must be a monomeric free radical. Also pentaphenylpentadienyl

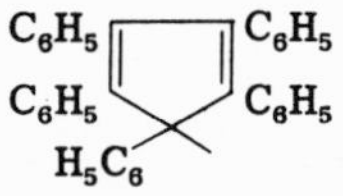

shows its radical nature in the solid state having the expected value of 1.73 Bohr magnetons.

In an analogous manner one can furnish proof for the existence of biradicals, having two uncompensated lone electrons, through the value

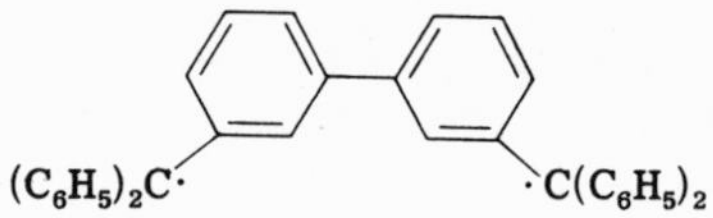

of $\sqrt{2(2+1)}\beta = \sqrt{6}\beta = 2.45\beta$ Bohr magnetons.[11] This is the case in Schlenck's hydrocarbon which, according to the formula
is a true biradical.[12] It is paramagnetic and has the expected value of 2.45 Bohr magnetons for two unpaired electrons. The fact that this compound appears as a biradical is explained in that saturation of the two free electrons would lead to a *meta*-quinoid structure. This is not possible since it would conflict with the valences. A more cogent proof is furnished by the introduction of four chlorine atoms in the *ortho* position in the hydrocarbon of Tschitschibabin. The resulting 2,2′,6,6′-tetrachloro-4,4′-bisdiphenyl-methylbiphenyl (III) is paramagnetic. The four *ortho* chlorine atoms prohibit coplanar orientation of the two phenyl rings so that the necessary double bond between them (I) cannot be formed. The two electrons remain unpaired and the molecule has a biradical structure.

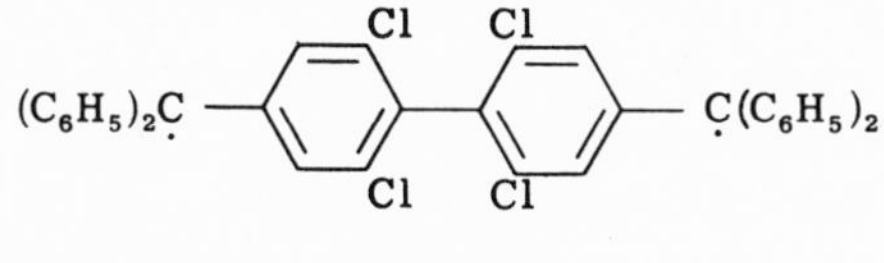

(III)

Porphyridin, first synthesized by Piloty,[13] is a most interesting compound which appears as a biradical within certain temperature limits. At low temperatures, porphyridin is diamagnetic; at room temperature and above it becomes paramagnetic. This phenomenon can be explained through a temperature dependent equilibrium between two structural formulas of porphyridin, (IV) and (V).

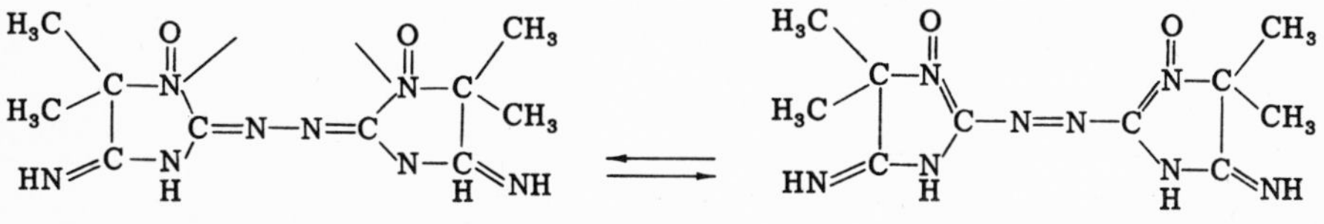

paramagnetic   diamagnetic
(IV)   (V)

[11] E. Müller, *Fortschr. chem. Forsch.* **1**, 326 (1949).

[12] Cf. comprehensive paper by E. Müller, *Z. angew. Chem.* **65**, 315 (1935).

[13] O. Piloty and W. Vogel, *Ber.* **36**, 1283 (1903); R. Kuhn, H. Katz, and W. Franke *Naturwissenschaften* **22**, 808 (1934); E. Müller and I. Müller-Rodloff, *Ann.* **521**, 81 (1935).

Structure (V) is diamagnetic, but structure (IV) is paramagnetic because each two N atoms have an unpaired electron which imparts to the molecule the structure of a nitrogen biradical.

The constitution of a metal ketylene[14] which is formed by the addition of alkali metals to nonenolizable ketones had been in doubt for some time.

$$2(C_6H_5)_2{=}C{\nearrow}^{OK} \rightleftharpoons (C_6H_5)_2{-}\underset{OK}{C}{-}\underset{OK}{C}{-}(C_6H_5)_2$$

The measurement of magnetic susceptibility furnished the proof of radicals. One can study the dissociation of metal ketyls as a function of mesomeric electron shifts and correlate it with the nature of substituents. Metal ketyls mutually saturate their free valence and form dimers which are derivatives of pinacolin.

The degree of dissociation depends on the nature of the substituents in the phenyl ring. While benzophenone potassium is present as a monomeric radical to 70%, the equilibrium is shifted by the introduction of two dimethylamino groups in the *para* positions to 100% in the direction of the free radical.

It is possible to prove the existence of free uncoupled electrons by a second method. It is based on the *ortho-para* hydrogen equilibrium which is influenced by compounds with radical character, i.e., with one or more unpaired electrons.[15] It is known that the hydrogen molecule appears in two modifications, *ortho-* and *para*-hydrogen. They differ in their nuclear spins and the connected magnetic nuclear moments, which are parallel in the *ortho* modification and antiparallel in the *para* modification. The two kinds of hydrogen molecules are in equilibrium with each other which, at ordinary temperature, is in the ratio of $o/p = 3/1$. The rate of attainment of this equilibrium can be catalyzed by certain substances such as active carbon and by paramagnetic compounds, as well as by H atoms and free radicals. If the pure modification is in contact with the free radical the slow rate of attainment of equilibrium is speeded up considerably. This catalytic action serves to show the presence of paramagnetism as well as to prove the radical nature of molecules. For example, NO, which possesses a lone uncoupled electron, acts as a catalyst on the *ortho-para* hydrogen

---

[14] W. Schlenk and T. Weickel, *Ber.* **44**, 1182 (1911); W. Schlenck and A. Thal, *ibid.* **46**, 2840 (1913).

[15] L. Farkas and H. Sachsse, *Z. physik. Chem.* **B23**, 19 (1933).

rearrangement and the same is observed with the typical free radicals triphenylmethyl and tribiphenylmethyl.[16]

In certain compounds there is a discrepancy between the results of this method and the determination of magnetic susceptibility. The above-mentioned hydrocarbon of Tschitschibabin proved to be diamagnetic when studied with the help of an external magnetic field. According to the *ortho-para* hydrogen rearrangement method, however, it should possess free uncoupled electrons since it catalyzes the attainment of equilibrium. The reason for this apparently contradictory behavior must lie in the fact that in the *ortho-para* hydrogen method, the H_2 molecules in the reaction kinetic transition phase approach molecules which possess unpaired electrons, resulting in the *ortho→para* H_2 conversion. The macroscopic magnetic method, however, determines the magnetic property of the entire molecule which, on the whole, may appear diamagnetic owing to two opposing permanent magnetic dipoles.[17] The situation is quite analogous to internal compensation of partial dipole moments such as, for example, in the case of *p*-dichlorobenzene. The total molecules appear electrically nonpolar in spite of the presence of partial moments which in the case of two opposing C—Cl moments are mutually compensated.

---

[16] G. M. Schwab and E. Agallidis, *Z. physik. Chem.* **B41,** 59 (1938); for demonstration of free radicals by ESR, cf. F. C. Nachod and W. D. Phillips, eds., "Determination of Organic Structures by Physical Methods," Vol. II, p. 617. Academic Press, New York, 1961.

[17] The catalytic conversion of *ortho-* to *para*-hydrogen on diamagnetic carbon probably belongs to the same category of phenomena. For theory cf. F. Kalckar and E. Teller, *Proc. Roy. Soc.* **A150,** 520 (1935); E. Wigner, *Z. physik. Chem.* **B23,** 28 (1938).

CHAPTER 19

The Influence of Electron Shifts on the Position of Chemical Equilibria

Electron shifts within a molecule which are caused by induction and mesomerism have an important influence on the value of the equilibrium constant in which these molecules participate. The systematic introduction of substituents which influence the position of an equilibrium may be followed by the study of these shift effects.

Particularly suitable for the study of electron shift effects are the dissociation equilibria of organic acids and bases. The study of the dependence of the nature of the substituents has been the subject of extended investigations. If one considers dissociation constants of acids and bases, respectively, as a function of chemical constitution[1] and relates them to mesomeric and resonance phenomena, one must take into account the energetic relationships between the physical constants and the shift effects. The dissociation (affinity) constant K is the ratio of the concentrations of the dissociated H^+ and X^- in equilibrium with the undissociated portions HX of an acid or base, respectively:

$$K = \frac{[H^+][X^-]}{[HX]}. \tag{67}$$

This constant is related to the second law of thermodynamics through the change of free energy of the dissociation process

$$\Delta F = -RT \ln K. \tag{68}$$

---

[1] Cf. H. C. Brown, D. H. McDaniel, and O. Häfliger, *in* "Determination of Organic Structures by Physical Methods" (E. A. Braude and F. C. Nachod, eds.), Vol. I, p. 567. Academic Press, New York, 1955.

The stabilization energy of the dissociation products, on the other hand, is a measure of the change in heat content ΔH of the system during the electron shift where $\Delta H = \Delta E - pdv$. Consequently, a comparison of resonance energy with the equilibrium constant K cannot be carried out immediately, but only if one takes into account the thermodynamical relationship:

$$\Delta F = \Delta H - T\Delta S \tag{69}$$

where ΔS is the entropy change in the dissociation process. If the corresponding values of Eq. (69) are introduced in Eq. (68), one obtains the expression for the equilibrium constant

$$\ln K = \frac{\Delta S}{R} - \frac{\Delta H}{RT},$$

and by integration:

$$K = e^{\Delta S/R} \cdot e^{-\Delta H/RT}. \tag{70}$$

They demonstrate that an acid or base is stronger, the greater the decrease in heat content and the higher the increase in entropy during the dissociation process. If one compares acids with bases which are not too different from each other constitutionally, the entropy change in the dissociation process may be assumed as equal. In the comparison in the first approximation, the dissociation constant may be related with the change in total energy and consequently with the resonance energy. Large dissociation constants correspond to large electronic shift energies. Before we discuss the influence of these shift effects on the acid strength, some electrostatic effects which are exerted by various charged groups must be considered.

The old concepts of acids and bases as compounds which can dissociate H^+ or OH^- ions, respectively (Arrhenius), has been extended by the theories of Lowry and Brønsted, which permit a better insight into ionic equilibria. According to Lowry[2] and Brønsted,[3] acids are substances which can donate protons and bases are proton acceptors. One and the same substance may be either an acid or a base depending on the reaction in which it is involved. In the following equilibria the molecules HCl and H_3O^- are acids because they may surrender protons, whereas as H_2O and Cl^- are bases since they can receive protons.

---

[2] T. M. Lowry, *Chem. & Ind.* (*London*) **42**, 43 (1923).
[3] J. N. Brønsted, *Rec. trav. chim.* **42**, 718 (1923).

	Acid		Base		Acid		Base
(1)	HCl	+	H_2O	$\rightleftharpoons$	H_3O^+	+	Cl^-
(2)	HSO_4^-	+	NH_3	$\rightleftharpoons$	NH_4^+	+	SO_4^{--}
(3)	$(C_6H_5)_3CH$	+	NH_2^-	$\rightleftharpoons$	NH_3	+	$(C_6H_5)_3C^-$
(4)	H_2O	+	H_2O	$\rightleftharpoons$	H_3O^+	+	OH^-

Each acid has a conjugate base and vice versa. One and the same substance, e.g., NH_3, may act in one particular equilibrium (2) as a base but in another (3) as an acid. Consequently, self-dissociation of the H_2O molecule [equilibrium (4)] indicates that one molecule must have acidic, and the other basic character.

Diprotic acids (formerly termed dibasic) dissociate in two steps and have two ionization (dissociation) constants. As a rule the second ionization constant is smaller than the first because in the first step a singly charged anion attracts the proton for the reverse reaction, i.e., the formation of undissociated acid. However, in the second step, the proton is attracted by a doubly charged anion in order to form the "acid anion."

$$(1) \quad H_2SO_4 \rightleftharpoons H^+ + HSO_4^-$$
$$(2) \quad HSO_4^- \rightleftharpoons H^+ + SO_4^{--}$$

Since there are two possibilities in the step for dissociation and only one possibility for capture of a proton, and in the second step, conversely, only one possibility to dissociate a proton but two possibilities for capture, the ratio of the *a priori* probabilities of dissociation of the first and second step should be 4:1. This then should be reflected in the ratio of the two dissociation constants, i.e., $K_1 = 4K_2$. Experimental data of diprotic dicarboxylic acids of the type

indicate that the ratio of the two ionization constants is larger than this factor 4. According to Bjerrum[4] it is possible to account for this fact through the electrostatic attraction of a carboxylic ion on the undissociated second carboxyl group. He formulated the equation

---

[4] N. Bjerrum, *Z. physik. Chem.* **106**, 219 (1923).

$$\ln \frac{K_1}{4K_2} = \frac{Ne^2}{RTDr^2} \tag{71}$$

where r is the distance between the two carboxylic groups, D is the dielectric constant of the medium, N is Avogadro's number, and e is the elementary charge of an electron. Since the equation uses the *a priori* factor 4 for the attraction effect, one can see that if $K_1 = 4K_2$ the effect becomes zero which may be realized if the distance between the carboxyl groups, r, approaches infinity. The difficulties in evaluation of this equation are found in the substitution of a correct value for the dielectric constant D. The value 80 for water only holds in a macroscopic plate distance of the condenser and may not be transferred directly to two charged carboxylic groups where the distance is of the order of magnitude of 10 Å. Because of the strong fields in the immediate environment of the ion, the largest number of the water molecules is oriented, and the dielectric constant for this small space between carboxylic acid groups may only amount to a few units. In an analogous fashion, Eucken[5] has pointed out that the effect of the substituents which causes a dipole moment must be taken into account in the dissociation of a proton. If μ is the dipole moment and ϑ the angle which this vector forms with the direction of the carboxyl group, the ratio of ionization constants of unsubstituted acid is given by the expression:

$$\ln \frac{Ks}{K} = \frac{Ne\,\mu\cos\vartheta}{RTDr^2}. \tag{72}$$

The right-hand side of Eq. (72) differs from Eq. (71) by the factor of $\mu\cos\vartheta$. In the place of the action of the total charge, e, of the electron, the charge of the partial moment μ in the direction of the carboxylic group, $\mu\cos\vartheta$, is used.

Ionization constants of aliphatic carboxylic acids have been the subject of extensive studies in the classical papers of Ostwald, where the dependence of acid strength had been explained on the basis of the nature and the position of the substituents. If one wishes to account for the influence of electron shift effects upon the acid nature of proton containing compounds, one may start by comparing the acidities of isoelectronic compounds in a series:

$$\overset{\displaystyle H}{\underset{\displaystyle H}{H\!:\!\overset{\displaystyle ..}{C}\!:\!H}} \quad , \quad \overset{\displaystyle H}{\underset{\displaystyle H}{H\!:\!\overset{\displaystyle ..}{N}\!:}} \quad , \quad \underset{\displaystyle H}{H\!:\!\overset{\displaystyle ..}{\underset{\displaystyle ..}{O}}\!:} \quad , \quad H\!:\!\overset{\displaystyle ..}{\underset{\displaystyle ..}{F}}\!:$$

[5] A. Eucken, *Z. angew. Chem.* **46**, 303 (1932).

The regular increase of acid character of the protons of the H atoms has already been dealt with above (cf. p. 112).

If one changes from an alcohol to the corresponding carboxylic acid, an increase in acidity is noted. This increase is explained as stabilization of the carboxylic ion through mesomeric charge exchange between the two O atoms according to the scheme:

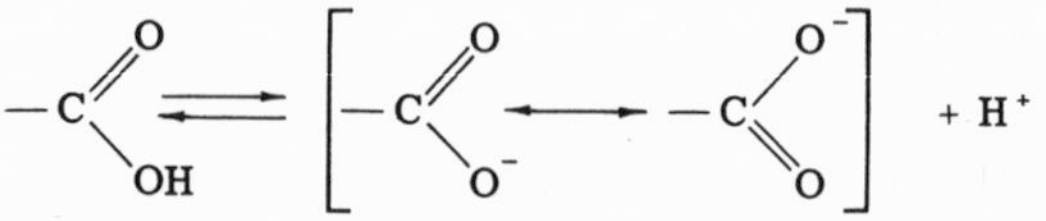

If in aliphatic carboxylic acids, the H atom is replaced by an electronegative substituent such as F, Cl, Br, or I, the acidity increases by a greater amount the closer the halogen is to the carboxylic acid group, and the larger the number of H atoms which are replaced by electronegative halogens. This regularity is apparent if one looks at the values shown in Table 24. One can explain the increase by an inductive removal of negative

TABLE 24

Ionization Constants of Weak Acids at 25°C

HCOOH	17.8×10^{-5}	C_6H_5COOH	6.27×10^{-5}
CH_3COOH	1.8×10^{-5}	$C_6H_5CH_2COOH$	4.88×10^{-5}
$ClCH_2COOH$	1.5×10^{-3}	$C_6H_5CH_2CH_2COOH$	2.19×10^{-5}
$Cl_2CHCOOH$	5.0×10^{-2}	$cis\text{-}C_6H_5CH{=}CHCOOH$	13.2×10^{-5}
Cl_3CCOOH	3.0×10^{-1}	$trans\text{-}C_6H_5CH{=}CHCOOH$	3.65×10^{-5}
CH_3CH_2COOH	1.4×10^{-5}	$trans\text{-}CH_3CH{=}CHCOOH$	2.03×10^{-5}
Butyric acid	1.5×10^{-5}	$CH_3C{\equiv}C{-}COOH$	2.22×10^{-3}
Valeric acid	1.6×10^{-5}	CH_3OH	10^{-16}
α-Chlorobutyric acid	1.39×10^{-3}	C_2H_5OH	10^{-18}
β-Chlorobutyric acid	8.1×10^{-5}	Phenylfluorene	10^{-21}
γ-Chlorobutyric acid	3.0×10^{-5}	Fluorene	10^{-25}
C_6H_5OH	1.09×10^{-10}	$(C_6H_5)_2NH$	10^{-23}
$p\text{-}NO_2C_6H_4COOH$	7.6×10^{-4}	$C_6H_5NH_2$	10^{-27}
Picric acid	1.6×10^{-1}	$(C_6H_5)_3CH$	10^{-33}

charges from the mesomeric carboxylic ion to the electronegative halogen. The carboxylic group becomes even more positive by the dissociation of the proton. The inductive shift is transmitted through the chain and its effect is reduced with the distance of the halogen from the carboxylic group as one might expect.

In the homologous series of aliphatic carboxylic acids, one finds an abrupt change of acid strength from the first member, formic acid ($K = 17.72 \times 10^{-5}$) to the next higher acid, acetic acid ($K = 1.7 \times 10^{-5}$), by a factor of 10. If the chain length is increased, this value changes but little and soon reaches a constant limiting value. According to the principles of electronic shift, which we have discussed before, the CH_3 group has a smaller electronegativity than the H atom which explains the decrease in acid strength. The methyl group possesses electron donor properties as we have discussed in Chapter 16. The replacement of the H atom in formic acid by a methyl group means the change of a $1s$-sp^2 bond to an sp^3-sp^2 bond. The trigonal sp^2 structure of the C atoms of the carboxylic group is due to the C=O bond. The spherical $1s$ cloud distribution of the electron in the H atom is replaced by the directional sp^3 hybrid of the CH_3 group which, owing to its vector properties, transfers negative charge to the neighboring, mesomerically equalized, carboxyl ion. The enhanced negative charge of the carboxyl group causes a decrease in acid strength since the ionization of the H atom is made more difficult electrostatically. A second effect which is additive and acts in the same direction is found in the hyperconjugation of the CH_3 group.

Introduction of a double bond in the neighborhood of the carboxyl group acts in the same sense as an electronegative halogen in enhancing the positive induction effect, $+J$, on the strength of the acid. Propionic acid has an ionization constant of 1.4×10^{-5} whereas acrylic acid is four times stronger ($K = 5.56 \times 10^{-5}$). The reason for the apparent higher electronegativity of the double bond is found in the replacement of the sp^3-sp^2 bond between the COOH group and the CH_2 group by an sp^2-sp^2 bond. The latter has a higher percentage s character owing to the spherical symmetry of the charge distribution which has a greater tendency to hold on to the electrons. The neighboring carboxyl group becomes more positive, and eases the dissociation of the H^+ ion. This then leads to a higher ionization constant. The inductive influence of a double bond is also seen in the decreasing effect of the double bond on the ionization of the acid, with increasing distance from the carboxyl group.

The influence of a phenyl ring in the chain belongs to the same category of phenomena. The phenyl group has a positive inductive effect on the

COOH group, as is shown in comparing the ionization constant of benzoic acid, C_6H_5COOH (6.27×10^{-5}), with the completely hydrogenated cyclohexane carboxylic acid, $C_6H_{11}COOH$ (1.34×10^{-5}). Hydrogenation changes the sp^2-sp^2 bond to a sp^3-sp^2 bond which must bring with it a decrease in acid strength as explained above. Introduction of a CH_2 group between the phenyl ring and the carboxylic acid causes a gradual decrease in acid strength, which also argues for the inductive character of the effect.

If one compares the ionization constants of the three acids: butyric acid, $CH_3CH_2CH_2COOH$ (1.5×10^{-5}); crotonic acid, $CH_3CH{=}CHCOOH$ (2.03×10^{-5}); and methylpropiolic acid, $CH_3C{\equiv}CCOOH$ (222.8×10^{-5}), one sees that replacement of an sp^2-sp^2 by an sp-sp^2 bond causes a marked 100-fold increase in acid strength. Introduction of a triple bond causes a percentage increase of s character of the above-mentioned bond. The transporting of negative charge away from the COOH group is purely inductive, as is shown by the decrease of the effect by successive introduction of several CH_2 groups.

Aside from this inductive effect, there still exists a mesomeric effect in the immediate neighborhood of double and triple bonds with the COOH group, which is based on the spreading and mutual overlap of the π electrons. This action is opposed to the one caused by the inductive effect, i.e., it produces a weakening of acid character because a flux of charge from the double bond towards the carboxyl group takes place. The increase in K which was observed in going to unsaturated acids must be the difference of both of these effects. The induction effect is stronger than the mesomeric effect. The latter can already be obliterated by introducing one CH_2 group, which removes coplanarity of the molecule. In the comparative series of aliphatic and aromatic alcohols and amines both effects are in the same direction. Whereas methyl alcohol, CH_3OH, has an ionization constant (in CH_3O^- and H^+) of 10^{-16}, the acid properties increase for aromatics, and phenol, C_6H_5OH, has an ionization constant of 1.06×10^{-10}. This abrupt increase is due to the concerted action of the two above effects. The replacement of the sp^3-$2p$ bond between the C and the O atoms in methanol by an sp^2-$2p$ bond in phenol (which has a negative influence on the oxygen) leads to a mesomeric spreading of the lone electrons of the O atoms over the π electrons of the phenyl radical. This produces a further transport of negative charge in the direction of the phenyl ring. The effect may be shown graphically as follows:

By introducing an electron acceptor into the phenyl ring, e.g., through an NO_2 group, the $-M$ effect is enhanced, and the ionization constant in p-nitrophenol increases further to 5.6×10^{-8}. The same regularities are found in the amine series in which the lone electrons of the nitrogen are in interaction with the π electrons of the phenyl ring. Their transport from the nitrogen towards the phenyl ring ($+M$ effect) hinders the addition of HCl according to the scheme:

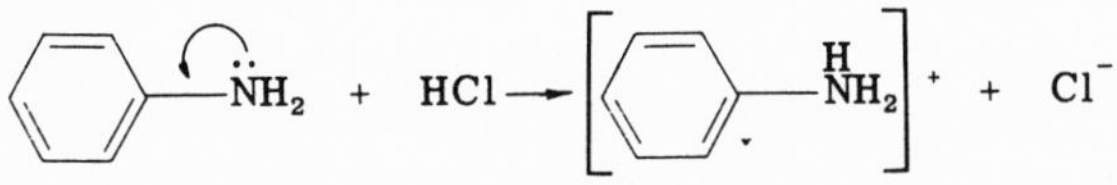

The basicity of aniline is therefore smaller than that of an alkylamine such as CH_3NH_2. Introduction of methyl groups causes an increase in basicity of the alkylamines, while successive replacement of H atoms with phenyl rings causes a decrease in basicity. This goes so far that triphenylamine, $(C_6H_5)_3N$, can no longer add HCl. Parallel with this goes the increase in acidity of the hydrogen atoms bound to the nitrogen. Diphenylamine, $(C_6H_5)_2NH$, can exchange its hydrogen against metallic potassium.

A similar increase in acidity is found in the series pyrrole

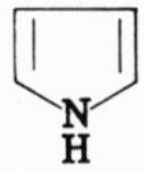

indole

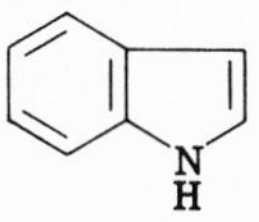

and carbazole

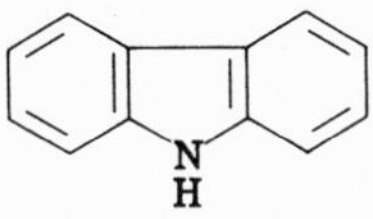

because the lone electron pair of the nitrogen interacts with an increasingly larger number of π electrons and the removal of charge increases with increasing number of phenyl rings.

The H atoms of the CH_3 group progressively acquire acid properties and can be given off in the form of protons if strong electron acceptors cause a decrease of CH bonds and lessening of bonding electrons. This can be found in the series toluene $C_6H_5CH_3$, diphenylmethane $(C_6H_5)_2CH_2$, and triphenylmethane $(C_6H_5)_3CH$. The last compound has the properties of a weak acid with an ionization constant of 10^{-33}. The hydrogen of the methyl group can be replaced with potassium. The acid properties of this hydrocarbon are even stronger if a nitro group, viz., a strong electron acceptor, is introduced. The p-trinitrotriphenylmethane forms a potassium compound $(p\text{-}NO_2\text{—}C_6H_4)_3CK$ which is not decomposed by alcohol.

The mesomeric electron exchange between the carboxyl group and an immediately neighboring double or triple bond $(+M$ effect) decreases ionization. This is only possible if carboxyl groups and double bonds lie in one plane. It can be followed by studying the ionization constants of stereoisomeric cis and trans-carboxylic acids. One finds that substituted ethylene carboxylic acids show an increase in acid strength provided that the spatial requirements of the substituents force them to twist outside of the plane defined by the ethylenic double bond, so that the molecule is no longer planar. The cis-dimethylethylene carboxylic acid

$$\begin{array}{c} H_3C-C-H \\ \parallel \\ H_3C-C-COOH \end{array}$$

is weaker (0.9×10^{-5}) than the trans compound

$$\begin{array}{c} H-C-CH_3 \\ \parallel \\ H_2C-C-COOH \end{array}$$

(5.1×10^{-5}). The same gradations are encountered in cis and trans isomers of chloroethylene and phenylcarboxylic acid.

Because of the above-mentioned influence of the hybrid bond on the dissociation of protons it must not be construed that the binding of the H atoms is less. Rather the opposite is the case, as can be shown in comparing the acidity of the hydrocarbons methane, ethylene, and acetylene with the overlap integrals of the sp^3-, sp^2-, and sp-hybrids with the $1s$ electron of hydrogen. The latter parameter $S_{AB} = \int \psi_A \psi_B d\tau$, is a measure for the bond strength of both atoms to which the electrons belong. The values for these overlap integrals are 0.72 for the CH bond in CH_4, 0.74 in ethylene, and 0.76 in acetylene.[6] They correspond to the gradations in ionization

---

[6] R. S. Mulliken, *J. Am. Chem. Soc.* **72,** 4493 (1950); A. D. Walsh, *Discussions Faraday Soc.* **2,** 18 (1947); L. Pauling, "The Nature of the Chemical Bond." Cornell Univ. Press, Ithaca, New York, 1940. For the wave-mechanical treatment of the polarization effects of ions, see J. G. Kirkwood, *Physik Z.* **33,** 259 (1932).

energy of these hydrocarbons into hydrogen atoms and radicals, e.g., $CH_4 \rightarrow CH_3 + H$. They indicate that the hydrogen atoms in acetylene are more strongly bound than in methane.

In contrast to this, acetylene has the ability to give off its hydrogen atoms in the form of ions. The higher acidity, in contrast to $CH_2{=}CH_2$ and CH_4, corresponds to the process $HC{\equiv}CH \rightarrow HC{\equiv}C^- + H^+$. It becomes apparent in the easy replacement of this hydrogen by metals (copper acetylene, $HC{\equiv}CCu$). If one bears in mind that the overlap integral refers to the electron clouds of the C and H atoms, respectively, and is an indication of the bond strength, the dissociation of a proton, bare of electrons, appears quite plausible.

Hammett[7] was successful in arriving at a quantitative expression for donor and acceptor properties of substituents with relation to the phenyl ring in a quantitative measure. He stated in 1935 that a linear relationship existed between the change of free energy of physical chemical equilibria, by introduction of substituents, and their electron affinity. It can be shown that if one plots the logarithm of a certain (reference) equilibrium against the logarithm of a second equilibrium in a series of substances in which the substituents are varied, a straight line results. Particularly in the *para* and *meta* derivatives of benzene, a sharp linearity was encountered which is expressed in the Hammett equation

$$\log K_1 = \rho \log K_2 + C. \tag{73}$$

The slope of the line, ρ, indicates the change of the free energy of the equilibrium in going from one substituent to the next. If the equilibrium constants of the nonsubstituted compounds for two equilibria are K_0 and K_0' and of the substituted compounds are K_s and K_s', respectively, one obtains by substitution the equation

$$\log \frac{K_s'}{K_0'} = \rho \log \frac{K_s}{K_0}. \tag{74}$$

Based on this equation, any given equilibrium can be chosen as a normal (reference) equilibrium and compared with all others. The ionization equilibrium of substituted benzoic acids is shown in Fig. 24. The ratio $\log K_s/K_0$ has been termed σ. It is the ratio of the ionization constants of substituted

---

[7] L. P. Hammett, *Chem. Revs.* **17**, 125 (1935); *Trans. Faraday Soc.* **34**, 156 (1938).

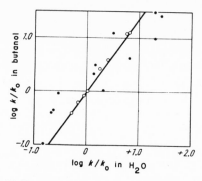

FIG. 24. Ionization constants in different solvents.

benzoic acids to benzoic acid itself on a logarithmic scale. Equation (74) can be written in the form

$$\log K_s'/K_0' = \rho\sigma \qquad (75)$$

where ρ and σ are constants. The constant σ is also called Hammett's constant and characterizes the change in the strength of the benzoic acid, caused by the substituents. It is related to the change in charge density at the point of dissociation caused by the action of the substituents. The constant ρ, on the other hand, is a measure of the responsiveness of the equilibrium if the charge density changes.

An evaluation of σ for a series of substituents in a large number of compounds has shown that they can be catalogued into two classes: one with positive and the other with negative signs. They are summarized in Table 25. It can be seen that the substituents with negative σ values are electron donors whereas substituents with positive σ values belong to electron acceptors. This does not hold for the halogens where induction and mesomeric effects may have opposing direction.

The NH$_2$ group, for example, in the *para* position has a σ value of -0.66. This means that the logarithm of the ionization constant of *p*-aminobenzoic acid is 0.66 times smaller than the logarithm of the ionization constant of benzoic acid itself. The NH$_2$ group in the *para* position hence weakens the acid strength by 0.66 logarithmic units. One finds the value $K = 1.34 \times 10^{-5}$ in contrast to $K_0 = 6.27 \times 10^{-5}$ for benzoic acid. On the other hand, the nitro group with a positive σ value of $+0.77$ increases the acid character by this amount. Increase or weakening of acid strength then, as can be readily derived, is related with the acceptor property of the NO$_2$ and the donor property of the NH$_2$ groups, respectively.

Since electron shifts fall into two categories, the inductive $\pm I$, and in the mesomeric $\pm M$, one might be tempted to separate σ values into two components, an inductive σ_I and a mesomeric σ_M portion. A possibility for this is furnished by the observation that σ values in the *meta* position are

TABLE 25
Hammett's σ Values

Substituent	σ value	Substituent	σ value
p-O⁻ . . .	-1.00	m-Cl . . .	$+0.372$
m-O⁻ . . .	-0.71	p-Br . . .	$+0.232$
p-NH₂ . . .	-0.66	m-Br . . .	$+0.931$
m-NH₂ . . .	-0.161	p-I . . .	$+0.276$
p-CH₃ . . .	-0.170	m-I	$+0.352$
m-CH₃ . . .	-0.069	p-NO₂	$+0.778$
p-OH . . .	-0.357	m-NO₂	$+0.710$
m-OH . . .	-0.002	p-CF₃	$+0.551$
p-OCH₃ . . .	-0.268	m-CF₃ . . .	$+0.415$
p-F . . .	$+0.062$	p-CN . . .	$+0.628$
m-F . . .	$+0.337$	m-CN . . .	$+0.678$
p-Cl . . .	$+0.228$	m-COH₃ . . .	$+0.115$

generally more positive than in the *para* position. In the case of OCH_3 groups one even notes a reversal of the sign of the σ value from -0.268 to $+0.115$. One ascribes the influence of a substituent in the *meta* position exclusively to an inductive effect, because as had been stated before, it is not possible to construct a *meta* quinoid structure.[*]

Another method for a separation of σ values into σ_I and σ_M has been proposed by Roberts.[8] He used the influence of the substituents in a fully hydrogenated acid like 4R-bicyclo-(2,2,2)-octane-1-oic acid:

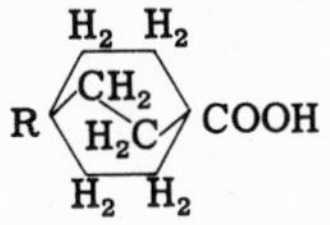

as a measure for the inductive effect. The selection of this rather complicated compound presumably was based on the belief that a field effect of the substituent R on the carboxylic acid could be eliminated by the interjection of three cyclohexane rings. Furthermore, the flexibility of simple

---

[*] Compare the absence of spectral change of polyphenylene in *m*-position, page 144.
[8] J. D. Roberts and W. T. Moreland, *J. Am. Chem. Soc.* **75**, 2167 (1953).

cyclohexane carboxylic acid (boat- and chair-form) which would have been sufficient from the view of elimination of double bonds, is impeded. The results of both methods, as well as the third one proposed by Taft[9] do not agree completely numerically. The reader is referred to the original papers.

It is surprising to note that the Hammett equation (74) also holds in an analogous fashion for the influence of substituents on reaction kinetics. In order to show this, one has to simply replace, in the above equations, the K of the equilibrium constant by a k for the rate constant, in order to demonstrate the linear dependence between the logarithm of the rate constant of the substituted with respect to the nonsubstituted compound. It is shown graphically in Fig. 25 for σ values of substituted benzenes. The

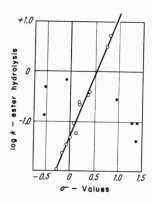

FIG. 25. Dependence of reaction velocity from Hammett's σ value.

reaction rate can be predicted.* This will be discussed further in the chapter on reaction kinetics.

For the *ortho*-substituted benzene derivatives one does not find a simple linear relationship in the sense of the Hammett equation. The reason for this can be found in the thermodynamic relation between affinity constant and resonance energy. Only in the case where the entropy changes in the two substances under comparison are the same, can such a relationship be expected. In the *ortho* derivatives this premise is not fulfilled since the order states are different.

---

* According to H. H. Jaffé [*Chem. Revs.* **53**, 191 (1953)], it is possible to calculate approximately 4,200 equilibrium or rate constants, respectively, on the basis of known σ- and ρ-constants.

[9] R. W. Taft, Jr., *in* "Steric Effects in Organic Chemistry" (M. S. Newman, ed.), p. 559. Wiley, New York, 1956.

CHAPTER 20

Color, Chemical Constitution, and Mesomerism[1]

One of the most interesting physicochemical problems is the inter-relationship between color and chemical constitution. A compound appears to be colored if it absorbs light selectivity, i.e., if a certain portion of the visible spectrum is absorbed by the compound and the complementary color is transmitted through it without change. The problem of the connection between color and chemical constitution then is reduced to the problem of the dependence of the absorption spectrum on the chemical nature of the compound.

The theories dealing with these problems have undergone many changes. However, present-day concepts of the nature of the color of substances permit one to make detailed statements about light absorption and the corresponding electronic changes, as they are reflected in chemical constitution.[2]

In 1868 Gräbe and Liebermann recognized that increasing numbers of double bonds conferred color to organic compounds, and 8 years later Witt first coined the term of chromophore, i.e., a color-carrying group, necessary for a substance to confer color character. Such groups have double and triple bonds such as $C=O$, $C\equiv N$, $N=N$, $N=O$, NO_2, and many others. Simultaneously Witt made the observation that a number of groups such as NH_2, CH_3, OH, and CH_3O which do not absorb in the visible range themselves, enhance the action of chromophoric groups. He introduced the term auxochromic (color-enhancing) group. With these two terms then the most important observations were recognized qualitatively. Later Armstrong, Bayer, and Wilstätter suggested that quinoid and meri-quinoid (= half-quinoid) structures were responsible for the color properties of

---

[1] Cf. Symposium on Color Chemistry, *Chimia* **15**, No.1, 4–226 (1961).

[2] Cf. E. A. Braude, *in* "Determination of Organic Structures by Physical Methods" (E. A. Braude and F. C. Nachod, eds.), Vol. I, p. 131. Academic Press, New York, 1955.

triphenylmethane dyestuffs and considered it as a chromophoric complex which hitherto had escaped notice. Dilthey (1920) separated chromophoric groups into contributing atoms, basing his thoughts on Pfeiffer's (1910) postulate of coordinate unsaturation for the production of chromophoric properties. These concepts were extended by Wizinger who suggested the term anti-auxochromic groups, i.e., groups which, in certain combinations, counteract the auxochromic groups and thereby diminish the color character.

Experiments to apply modern electronic theory of organic compounds to dyestuffs are only fairly recent and are based on Pauling's ideas on resonance stabilization in valence structures. F. Arndt and B. Eistert[3] introduced the concept of mesomerism into dyestuff chemistry in 1948. Their ideas, however, met with certain difficulties and were supplanted by the concepts that the difference in resonance energies between the ground and excited states were color determining. This difference has been calculated in many cases, based on empirical data with the use of the VB method (Sklar,[4] Förster,[5] Seel,[6] and others) as well as with the MO method (Hückel,[7] Mulliken[8]).

A prediction of the position of the absorption band of organic compounds was first carried out by H. Kuhn in 1948 who treated the delocalized electrons present in mesomeric molecules like an electron gas and applied the Sommerfeld electron theory of metals.

The absorption in the visible and near ultraviolet light, of interest to the chemist, is based on a promotion of electrons from the normal to higher energy levels. This electronic excitation corresponds energetically to a discrete wavelength, $\Delta E = h\nu$. In the liquid or dissolved state, owing to the action of neighboring molecules, this is generally a broad and more or less continuous absorption band with a more or less developed maximum. It is characterized by the wavelength of the maximum, λ_{max}, and the intensity of the absorption which is expressed by the absorption coefficient ϵ_{max} (also A_M) at the same wavelength. It is defined by the equation

$$I = I_0 e^{-\epsilon c d}$$

[3] See B. Eistert, "Chemismus und Konstitution." Enke, Stuttgart, 1948.

[4] A. L. Sklar, *J. Chem. Phys.* **5**, 669 (1937); *Revs. Modern Phys.* **14**, 232 (1942).

[5] T. Förster, *Z. physik. Chem.* **B41**, 287 (1938); *Z. Elektrochem.* **45**, 548 (1939).

[6] F. Seel, *Naturwissenschaften* **34**, 124 (1947); *Z. Naturforsch.* **3a**, 180 (1948).

[7] E. Hückel, *Z. physik. Chem.* **B34**, 339 (1936); *Z. Elektrochem.* **43**, 752 (1937).

[8] R. S. Mulliken and C. A. Rieke, *Repts. Progr. in Phys.* **8**, 231 (1941).

Here I_0 is the initial intensity of the incident light beam and I is the intensity after passing through a thickness d (in centimeters) of a solution of concentration c (in molarity). ϵ is a characteristic absorption coefficient for the substance under observation. It represents a layer of thickness at which the intensity of the incident beam I_0 is reduced to the eth portion at the concentration c. Numerically this value can reach 40,000 or more and is strongly dependent on the wavelength. We shall follow the variations of these two parameters λ_{max} and ϵ_{max} with chemical constitution, using selected examples, and pay particular attention to the type of chemical bond in the classifications used previously.

The position of absorption in saturated paraffins which contain only σ bonds is in the far ultraviolet below 1500 A, because bonds are not easily excited. Replacement of H atoms by CH_3 groups causes a shift of light absorption towards longer wavelengths. Such substituents, whose action can be followed in various atomic groups, are called bathychromic,* i.e., color deepening. Water absorbs in the far ultraviolet and this absorption is ascribed to a promotion of one of the octet electrons of the O atoms to a higher energy level. If the OH group becomes negative by the dissociation of a proton, one observes a red shift and the absorption moves towards 1680 Å for the OH-ion. A loosening of the octet through the negative charge is believed to be responsible. The same phenomenon of enrichment of the O octet with negative charge is encountered in the replacement of an H atom with electron donating CH_3 groups. The replacement of two ($1s$-sp) bonds in H_2O with two sp^3-sp bonds in dimethyl ether causes a negative charge shift of the CH_3 groups toward the O atom and is accompanied by a red shift in the absorption to 1900 Å.

Analogous regularities are found in sulfur and nitrogen compounds. Dissociation of H_2S to the acid anion HS^- is accompanied by a shift of absorption from 1890 Å to 2270 Å where the absorption intensity remains approximately constant, log ϵ_{max} = 3.5. The electron donating group, CH_3, shifts the absorption maximum in the same direction. However, if a proton is added to the lone electron pair of nitrogen in ammonia or in an amine, the N electron octet becomes positive, contracts, and strengthens with a concomitant shift of the absorption maximum to a shorter wavelength. This action of substituents is called a hypsochromic effect. The methyl group again acts bathychromically, as is shown in the change from

---

* In this book the correct word *bathychromic* ($\beta\alpha\theta\acute{v}\chi\rho\omega\mu$os) will be used instead of the more common but incorrect *bathochromic*.

ammonia to methylamine, or from halogen halides HCl, HBr, HI to the corresponding methyl halides.

A double bond, as we have seen, consists of a σ and a π bond. The space distribution of the π electrons is such that they are further away from the positively charged C skeleton, on the average, than the electrons of a σ bond. π electrons thus have a greater mobility. This is shown, for example, in the double bond increment of the molar refraction. The loose bond of the π electrons means that less energy is necessary for its excitation to a higher energy level. The first absorption maximum is found at longer wavelengths than in the case of saturated compounds, which is demonstrated in the large number of absorption spectra of unsaturated compounds.

The statement that the number of double bonds deepens the color is one of the earliest observations in the field of color of organic substances. An additional bathychromic effect is encountered if the double bonds are conjugated. The absorption maxima of diphenylpolyenes[9] increase regularly with increasing number of members towards longer wavelengths, which can be expressed by the empirical correlation $\lambda_{max} = K_1 \sqrt{n} + K_2$, where n is the number of double bonds and K_1 and K_2 are constants.

The phenyl ring must be considered as a chromophore in its own right. The type of connection of the phenyl ring with higher hydrocarbons is of importance regarding the color of the resulting compounds. While a *meta* position has no influence upon the position of the first absorption maximum* a *para* substitution has a decided bathychromic effect. One notes a shift of the absorption maximum from biphenyl (2500 Å) to hexaphenyl (3180 Å). In the closer coupling of phenyl rings, as is found in the condensed ring systems where coplanarity is certain, a marked and strong red shift is noted. Much less activation energy is necessary for the delocalized electrons as can be shown in the color of the acenes. Characteristically the deepening of the color by annulation of phenyl rings is less pronounced if it is carried out in angles. Whereas tetracene

is orange yellow, triphenylene

---

* Cf. the splitting of Hammett's σ values into σ_I and σ_M, based on the σ constants of the *meta* derivatives, p.

[9] R. Kuhn et al., Z. physik. Chem. **B29**, 391 (1935).

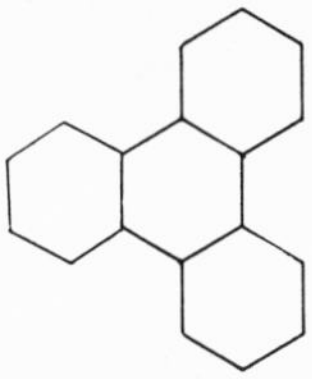

is colorless. Similarly perylene

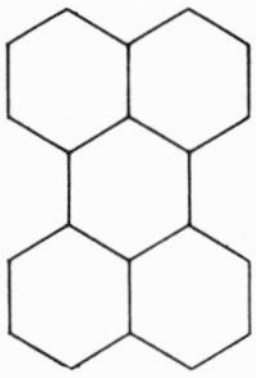

has no color whereas the solid pentacene

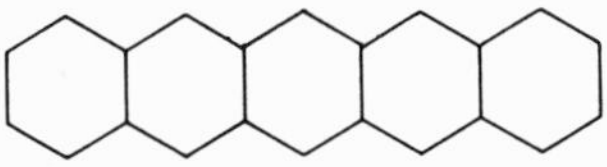

is intensely violet. In analogous fashion, one can follow the chromophoric properties of other elements and study the bathychromic or hypsochromic influence of various substituents respectively. Two nitrogens connected with a double bond are a stronger chromophore than a C=C bond. The reason for this is easily recognized because aside from the σ and π bonds, there is a lone electron pair on each N which, as we have noted before (p. 143), accounts for a shift of the first absorption maximum towards longer wavelengths. Azo compounds already absorb at 3500, whereas the corresponding C=C compounds start to absorb just below 2000 Å. The spectrum is moved still further towards the red as soon as the double bond involves two dissimilar atoms such as N and O. Nitroso compounds are a good example: trimethylnitrosomethane

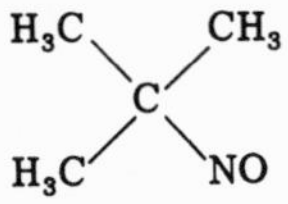

absorbs at 6660 Å. This must be ascribed to the electron donating action of three methyl groups in concerted action with the NO group. The same phenomena are observed in the case of ketones. Whereas acetone, CH_3COCH_3, absorbs at 2730 Å, the substitution of the six H atoms with six methyl groups produces a red shift of approximately 220 A. Direct annulation of keto groups deepens color considerably, as is shown by the orange-red color of 2,3,4-triketopentane:

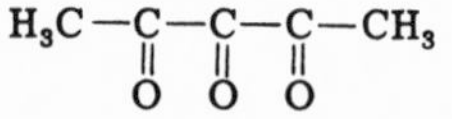

$$H_3C-\underset{\underset{O}{\|}}{C}-\underset{\underset{O}{\|}}{C}-\underset{\underset{O}{\|}}{C}-CH_3$$

However, if the keto groups are separated by CH_2 groups the absorption falls back to the one of acetone. The hypsochromic effect of the CH_2 group must be ascribed to the removal of conjugation and coplanarity of the $C{=}O$ groups, a phenomenon which is repeated in the various combinations of atoms in the same direction. Biphenyl, for example, shows a different absorption than benzene which disappears if a CH_2 group is interjected, as in the case of diphenylmethane. The resulting spectrum again resembles benzene. Similarly, the spectrum of diphenylamine no longer shows the contour of the benzene spectrum (cf. Figs. 12 and 13). The molecule has the form of a flattened pyramid so that the π electrons of the phenyl groups and the lone electron pair of the nitrogen are almost in a plane and may be in resonance with each other. Coplanar orientation of both phenyl rings may not only be destroyed by interposing of a CH_2 group, as had been discussed earlier in the chapter on dipole moments, but also by substitution with *ortho* CH_3 groups.

The bathychromic action of annulation of benzene rings in the acenes can be obliterated by hydrogenation of a benzene ring at or near the mid-position. If one hydrogenates hexacene

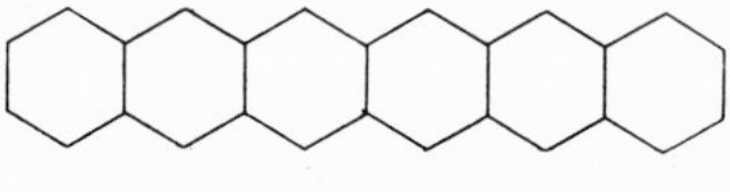

in positions 6 and 15, the conjugation across the total molecule is removed. The result in essence is an anthracene and a naphthalene molecule coupled by two CH_2 groups:

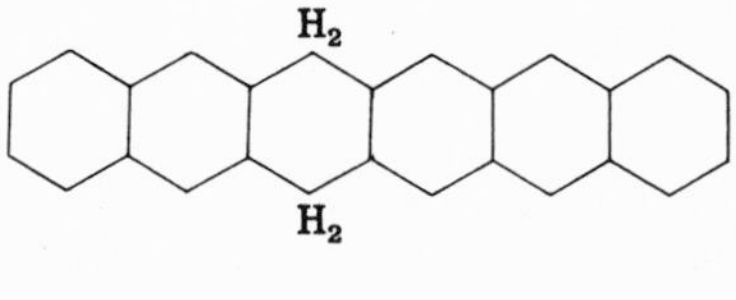

In the absorption spectrum, the 6,15-dihydrohexacene behaves like an equimolar mixture of naphthalene and anthracene. The same views hold for the removal of conjugation and coplanarity in going from compound

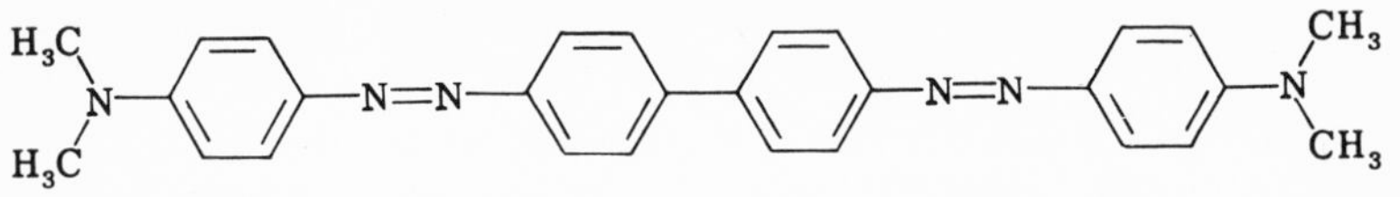

to

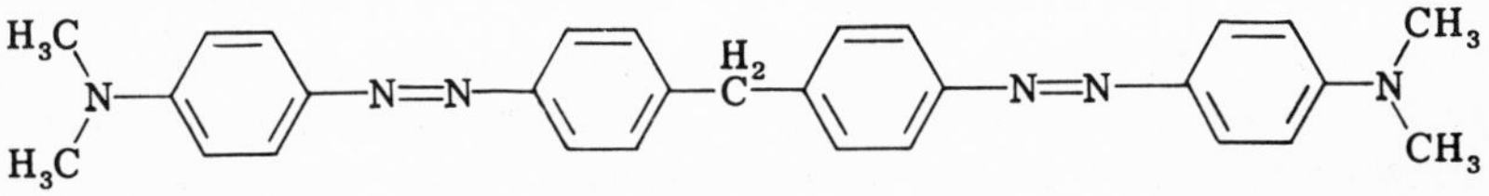

with a parallel change in absorption spectra. The fact that natural rubber, which is a high polymer with a large number of double bonds, has no color is based on the lack of conjugation by interposition of CH_2 groups.

These purely qualitative gradations, contain certain regularities which do not permit quantitative predictions of the position of frequency of an absorption band of a substance, based on its chemical constitution. However they must serve as a basis for any quantitative theory which is concerned with the basic reasons of the influence of color through substituents.

The first attempts in this direction are the theories of Slater, Pauling, and Hückel. They are based on the energy differences between the ground and excited states and their reflection in the differences between resonance hybrids. As had been explained earlier (p. 66), resonance energy is the energy difference between the valence hybrid and the energetically lowest canonical structure. The resonance energy increases with an increase in the number of canonical structures producing the hybrid. Color has nothing to do with the resonance energy of the ground state alone. This can be shown in a number of examples. The resonance energy of benzene is approximately 40 kcal/mol, of fulvene

calculated according to the MO method, 27 kcal/mol. Nevertheless, this molecule* absorbs in the visible region but benzene only near 2500 Å. An

---

* Unsubstituted fulvene is a yellow, unstable oil.

analogy is found in the relationship between naphthalene and its isomeric azulene,

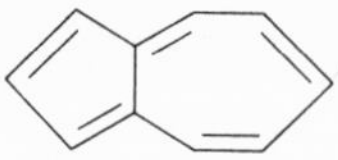

which has a blue color, in spite of the fact that its resonance energy is less than the colorless naphthalene.

One must assume, according to the theory, that the excited state which is caused by light absorption is stabilized by resonance, whereby polar limiting structures play a preferential role. The reason for the latter is found in the fact that light absorption is concomitant with a shift of electronic charge and hence with production of polarity. Using this scheme, it is possible to explain bathychromic action in the simple conjugated hydrocarbons. With an increasing number of double bonds, the resonance energy of the ground as well as of the excited state is increased. However, the number of polar structures in the excited state increases much more rapidly with an increasing number of double bonds and hence the resonance energy of the excited state increases faster than that of the ground state. Consequently, the energy difference between the ground state and excited states decreases with an increasing number of double bonds which means a red shift of the first absorption maximum. This may be demonstrated in some examples.

Ethylene, $CH_2{=}CH_2$, in the excited state has two polar structures of equal energy which form a hybrid:

$$H_2\overset{+}{C}{-}\overset{-}{C}H_2 \longleftrightarrow H_2\overset{-}{C}{-}\overset{+}{C}H_2$$

In butadiene the number of these polar structures increases to six, in contrast to the two canonical limiting structures in the ground state (I):

Ground state

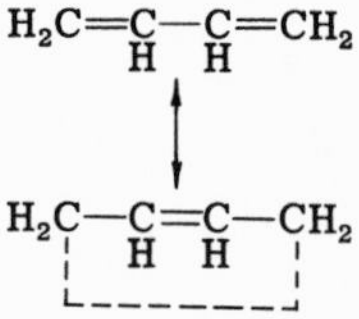

(I)

Excited state

$$\overset{-}{H_2}\overset{+}{C}-\overset{-}{C}H-CH=CH_2 \longleftrightarrow H_2C=CH-\overset{+}{C}H-\overset{-}{C}H_2$$

$$\overset{+}{H_2}C-CH=CH-\overset{-}{C}H_2$$

(II)

Resonance stabilization of the excited hybrid (II) is greater than that of the ground state. The same is repeated to a larger degree in the hydrocarbons with a greater number of conjugated double bonds. The energy difference of both hybrids must decrease steadily. This explanation of the bathychromic effect of conjugated double bonds according to Slater and Pauling is visualized in Fig. 26. In this manner one obtains a gradation of

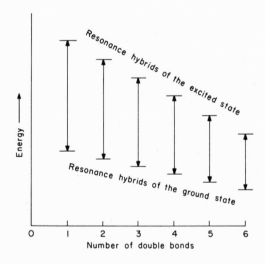

FIG. 26. Explanation of the bathychromic effect of conjugated double bonds.

the first absorption maximum of the dienes from ethylene (1600 Å) to octatriene (3000 Å).

If one tries to apply this principle to complex compounds, one encounters contradictions and exceptions. In the absence of steric hindrance and with growing molecular dimensions, the rapid increase of numbers of polar structures should lead to a steady red shift of the first absorption maximum. (For benzene alone 172 polar structures can be written.) In contrast to this, the absorption spectra of benzofulvene

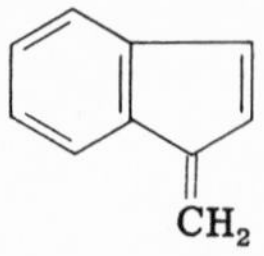

and dibenzofulvene

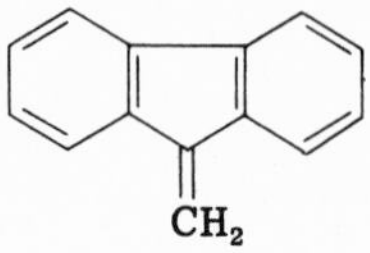

in comparison with fulvene

lie further in the violet and do not display the postulated red shift. This discrepancy is still more pronounced in going from porphyrin to tetradro-porphyrin, (III)–(IV). The hydrogenated product absorbs at a longer

λ_{max}
6300 Å

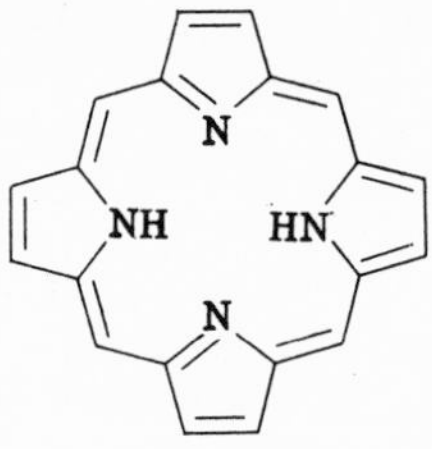

λ_{max}
8000 Å

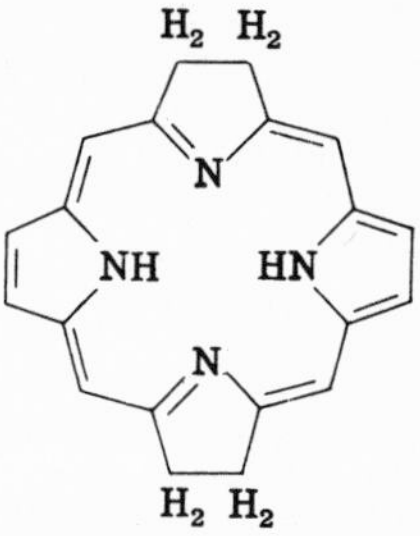

(III)   (IV)

wavelength than the nonhydrogenated one. Since hydrogenation reduces the number of canonical structures and the number of polar structures, there must be a principal defect in the argument.

Mulliken[10] ascribed to the long wavelength absorption maximum an

---

[10] R. S. Mulliken and C. A. Rieke, *Repts. Progr. in Phys.* **8**, 231 (1941).

electronic transition from the highest bonding to the lowest nonbonding
energy level. The energy levels were calculated according to the MO
method and can be defined for a molecule having π electrons by:

$$E = Q + m\gamma. \tag{75a}$$

This equation is analogous to Eq. (55) in which Q is the Coulombic attraction energy, γ is the resonance integral, and m is a coefficient. On account
of the excited states, it is necessary to take the overlap integral S into
account. As a sequel to this, the bonding and antibonding electronic states
are no longer symmetrical to the zero line ($m = 0$). The antibonding states
assume relatively higher energy levels. Owing to calculation difficulties
the parameter γ is derived from empirical data and fed into the equation.
Therefore separate γ values are necessary for each homologous series.

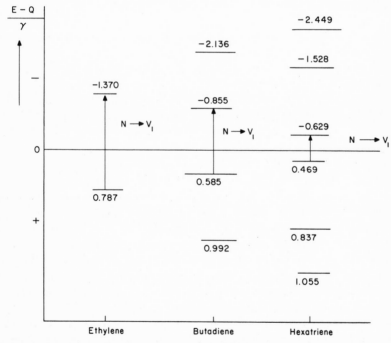

FIG. 27. Energy terms of bonding and antibonding states.

The energy levels of the bonding and anti-bonding states for ethylene,
butadiene, and hexatriene are shown schematically in Fig. 27. One recog-

nizes that the red shift of the first absorption maximum is correctly corre-
lated with the number of conjugated double bonds. The energy differences
between the highest bonding and the lowest antibonding state, which,
according to Mulliken, are called N → V transitions, decrease in the series
ethylene, butadiene, and hexatriene.

The energy levels of substituted fulvenes (Fig. 28) (fulvene, I; benzofulvene, II; dibenzofulvene, III; and dinaphthofulvene, IV) show that there

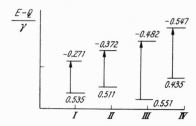

FIG. 28. Energy terms of bonding and antibonding states of fulvenes.

is no simple relationship between the magnitude of the conjugated double
bond system and its absorption in the longest wavelength range, as might
be postulated from the number of canonical structures. The scheme shows
that the first absorption maximum of dibenzofulvene is in the shortest
wavelength range compared with the other fulvenes, in agreement with
observation.

The described N → V transitions are not always the longest wavelength
absorptions. In the carbonyl and thiocarbonyl compounds, the absorption
can be related to the transition of one of the electrons of the lone electron
pair of the S or O atom, respectively, to the antibonding π^*- or σ^*-level,
respectively. They are termed N → A-$(2p$-$\pi^*)$ and N → B-$(2p$-$\sigma^*)$ transitions, respectively. The justification for such a correlation is found in the
experimental observation[11] that the first ionization potential of this compound corresponds numerically with these transitions.

Sterical factors may influence not only the position of the absorption
maxima, but also their magnitude. Several interesting cases have been
reported by Pickett and Rodebusch (1940) and will be discussed below.
These authors ascertained the sequence given in (V) for the height and
position of absorption in substituted benzaldehyde and benzophenones,
respectively.

[11] R. S. Mulliken, *J. Chem. Phys.* **3**, 504 (1935).

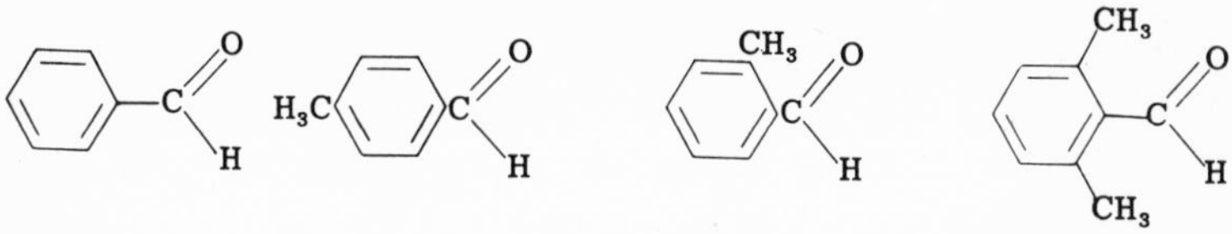

λ_{max} (Å)	2420	2510	2510	2510
ϵ_{max}	14,000	15,000	13,000	12,000

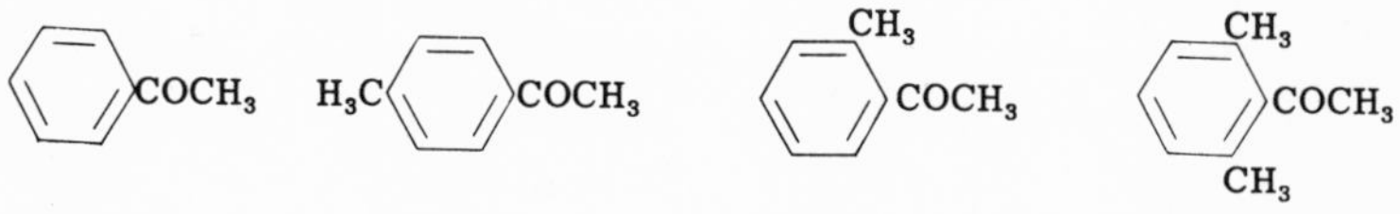

λ_{max} (Å)	2410	2430	2410	2410
ϵ_{max}	13,000	15,500	8500	5500

(V)

In both the benzaldehyde and the benzophenone series, the position of the absorption maximum is hardly influenced by the position of the substituted CH_3 groups. However, the absorption intensity steadily decreases as the CH_3 group moves towards the aldehyde or keto group, respectively. For o-disubstituted methyl derivatives, the decrease is the most pronounced. The height of the absorption maximum in the aldehydes is only $\frac{3}{4}$, and in the ketones only approximately $\frac{1}{3}$ of the absorption of the corresponding compounds with p-substituted CH_3 groups. This, of course, must be the steric effect of the o-substituted CH_3 groups, which has a complicated influence on the intensity of the absorption.

The explanation given by Braude[12] goes along the following lines: The decrease in intensity is ascribed to a prohibited electronic transition between the nonplanar arrangement of the phenyl and carboxyl groups in the ground state, and the planar arrangement in the excited state. Because of mesomerism, the phenyl plane and the $C=O$ plane have the tendency to be coplanar to each other. On the other hand, in the ground state there is free rotation around the σ bond, as well as torsional vibrations along this axis. In the excited state, the free rotation is largely inhibited because an electronic transition has taken place between the phenyl and carboxyl

[12] E. A. Braude, E. R. H. Jones, H. P. Koch, R. W. Richardson, F. Sondheimer and J. B. Toogood, *J. Chem. Soc.* p. 1890 (1949); E. A. Braude and F. Sondheimer, *ibid.* p. 3754 (1955); L. H. Schwartzmann and B. B. Corson, *J. Am. Chem. Soc.* **76**, 781 (1954); G. D. Hedden and W. G. Brown, *ibid.* **75**, 3744 (1953). Cf. however R. B. Turner and D. W. Voitle, *ibid.* **73**, 1403 (1951).

groups, establishing a quasi-double bond between these groups. This diminishes the amplitude of the torsion vibration. Of lesser importance is the vibration along the connecting axis on account of steric hindrance if two CH_3 groups are in the *ortho* position. These relationships can best be seen from a graphic representation of the potential course of the molecule in a torsion vibration in the electronic ground and excited states. In Fig. 29, the ordinate denotes the potential energy, the abscissa the angle ϑ

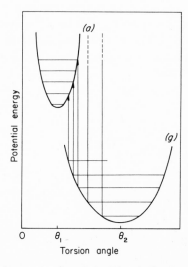

Fig. 29. Demonstration of the Franck-Condon principle.

between the phenyl and carboxyl groups, around which torsion vibrations take place. One can see from this figure that trough (a) is considerably higher than trough (g) and displaced towards smaller angles. Furthermore, it is smaller, corresponding to the formed quasi-double bond and the resulting smaller amplitudes of torsion vibration. The latter fact has an important influence upon the intensity of the absorption. The number of vertical lines may serve as a measure of the intensity of absorption because they connect the ground state with the vibrational levels of the excited state. These tie-lines can only be vertical because the molecule during its electronic transition (about 10^{-8} sec) has no time to undergo vibrations with its 2000 times more inert masses (Franck-Condon principle).[13] This restriction holds

---

[13] J. Franck, *Trans. Faraday Soc.* **21**, 536 (1926); E. U. Condon, *Phys. Rev.* **28**, 1182 (1926); **32**, 858 (1928).

only because the heavy atomic masses cannot follow a much more rapid electronic motion. The narrower the upper potential curve, the lesser the number of vibrational states in the ground state which find their counterpart in the excited state. This means a decrease in intensity, which must be larger the more the spatial requirements of the o-CH$_3$ group diminishes the torsion amplitude of the phenyl group against the CO group.

A considerable advantage in the direction of a quantitative calculation and prediction of the position of the absorption maximum of organic compounds is found in the application of the electron theory of metals (Sommerfeld) which treats the π electrons of a mesomeric molecule as an electron gas (cf. H. Kuhn and others[14]). The state of the electron gas is realized because the delocalized π electrons are considered freely mobile within the molecular skeleton, whose boundaries cannot be crossed owing to high potentials. The calculation of the first absorption maximum in a simplified one-dimensional electron gas model is carried out along the following lines:

The wave equation of an electron which can move freely along the length L, the ends of which have an infinitely high potential V, may be written in the following form (cf. Fig. 30):

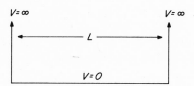

Fig. 30 One-dimensional electron box model.

$$\frac{d^2\psi}{ds^2} + \frac{8\pi^2 m}{h^2}(E - V_s)\psi = 0. \tag{76}$$

The limiting condition for the potential energy is:

$V = 0$ for $0 < s < L$

$V = \infty$ for $L < s$ and $s < 0$.

This then means that the electron within the linear box has a potential energy V of zero whereas outside of it ($s > L$) the value becomes infinity.

---

[14] H. Kuhn, *Helv. Chim. Acta* **31**, 1441 (1948); N. S. Bayliss, *J. Chem. Phys.* **16**, 287 (1948); W. T. Simpson, *ibid.* p. 1124; I. R. Platt, *ibid.* **17**, 484 (1949).

The papers of O. Schmidt [*Z. Elektrochem.* **43**, 238 (1937); *Z. physik. Chem.* **B39**, 76 (1938); **B42**, 83 and 106 (1939); **B44**, 194 (1939); *Ber.* **73**, 97 (1940)] must be considered as a landmark for the treatment of π-electrons as a degenerate electron gas.

The electron is then practically confined in the box. If these limiting conditions are obeyed, one finds solutions for the wave function:

$$\psi_n = \sqrt{\frac{2}{L}} \sin \frac{\pi s}{L}\, n, \tag{77}$$

wherein n is a quantum number which can only take the integers 1, 2, 3, ... The eigenvalues of the energy E_n which are finite, steady, and single-valued solutions for this equation are given by the expression:

$$E_n = \frac{h^2 n^2}{8mL^2}. \tag{78}$$

One may note that the length of the box L, i.e., the dimensions of the molecule, is given in the energy equation. Equation (78) gives the levels of the discrete energy states, regardless of whether they are occupied by electrons or not.

If one feeds a certain number N of electrons into this box, according to the Pauli exclusion principle, only two electrons may belong to each energy state, differing only in the orientation of the spin. A third entering electron necessarily must be placed on a higher energy level. Consequently the largest quantum number occurring in the electron gas, n, must be equal to half the number of the freely moving π electrons, i.e., $N/2$. After introduction of the Pauli principle, the energy equation (78) is now rewritten as:

$$E_n = E_{N/2} = \frac{h^2}{8mL^2}\left(\frac{N}{2}\right)^2. \tag{79}$$

The process of light absorption consists in the transition of a π electron from the highest occupied energy level $E_{N/2}$ to the next higher one which is either unoccupied or half occupied, $E_{(N/2)+1}$. The energy difference of these levels ΔE corresponds to the absorbed light quantum $h\nu$. This leads to the equation:

$$\Delta E = h\nu = E_{(N/2)+1} - E_{N/2} = \frac{h^2}{8mL^2}(N+1). \tag{80}$$

If one replaces the length of the box, L, with the length of a linear molecule with conjugated double bonds, one may write: $L = N \times l$, where l represents the distance between two C atoms and N the number of the C atoms. The latter is equal to the number of electrons, because a freely moving electron can be ascribed to each C atom. The final form for Eq. (80), solved for wavelength λ of the absorbed light, is:

$$\lambda_{max} = \frac{8mcN^2l^2}{h(N+1)}. \tag{81}$$

The important result of this simple calculation of an absorbing molecule consists in the fact that for the first time a numerical relationship has been established between λ_{max}, i.e., the color of the molecule, and the number of the electrons and atomic distances between which these electrons move about freely.

One recognizes readily that Eq. (81) describes the bathychromic effect of an increasing number of conjugated double bonds very well, in correspondence with experimental facts. With increasing N, λ_{max} increases too. The absorption spectrum moves towards longer wavelengths.

TABLE 26

Red Shift of the Absorption Maximum with Increasing Number of π-Electrons

N	λ_{theor} (Å)	λ_{exp} (Å)
10	5750	5900
12	7060	7100
14	8340	8200
16	9590	9300

Table 26 shows a comparison of calculated and experimentally found positions of the absorption maxima as a function of the number N of the π electrons.

The cyanine dyestuffs may serve as a chemical example for the one-dimensional electron gas model. Two ring systems are connected with a polymethene chain of variable length while the atomic distances along this chain are equalized through delocalization of the π electrons. For the distance between the C atoms along which the π electrons move about freely, one uses the value 1.39 Å, corresponding to the bond order 1.5 between the C atoms in the polymethene chain. The measurements of Brooker[15] show that the absorption maximum at 4450 Å is in good agreement with the calculation which furnishes a value of 4530 Å.

The influence of the end phenyl rings must be taken into account in a special manner. Since the π electrons of the phenyl groups are polarizable,

---

[15] L. C. S. Brooker, *Revs. Modern Phys.* **14**, 275 (1942).

the course of the potential towards the end of the chains is less steep than in the idealized box model in which the potential walls are perpendicular. This gradual increase leads to an extension of the chain. H. Kuhn has determined this lengthening empirically as $\frac{2}{3}l$ by starting with the first member of the polymethene chain for the absorption position and then calculating back to the position L. This leads to better agreement in the higher members of the series. The influence of a p-nitro group which acts as an electron acceptor likewise must be taken into account by an extension of the chain. One uses as the length for the box the expression $L = (N + 1) \times l$. The agreement between calculation and measurement for the series can be

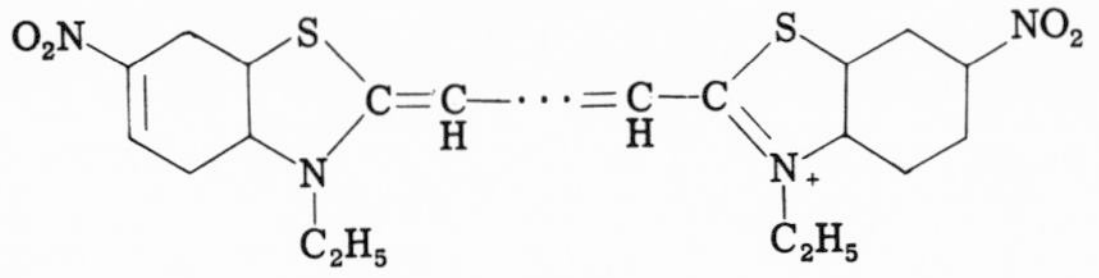

seen in Table 27.

TABLE 27
Red Shift of the Absorption Maximum with Increasing Number of π-Electrons

N	$\lambda_{Calc._{max}}$ (Å)	$\lambda_{Obs._{max}}$ (Å)
6	4460	4500
8	5740	5800
10	7010	6800

If one calculates the absorption maxima using Sklar's approximation, one must assume incredibly high resonance energies for the cyanine dye-stuffs. Also the MO method of Mulliken does not give good agreement regarding the position of the absorption maxima.

One can demonstrate the influence of quantum mechanical viewpoints on the dyestuff chemistry particularly well by considering the variation of light absorption of a polymethene chain by various substituents. If a heteroatom such as, for example, nitrogen is introduced in the conjugated carbon chain, the electron gas is disturbed. This has an effect on light absorption. Introduction of an N atom in the polymethene chain causes a red or violet shift of the first absorption maximum depending on whether the chain has an even or odd number of double bonds. Furthermore, the manner of the shift depends on the position at which the N atom was introduced into the chain. Let us consider a symmetrical polymethene of the structure given in (VI) in order to derive the connection qualitatively. Its eight π elec-

$$H_3C\diagdown \atop H_3C\diagup N-\underset{H}{C}=\underset{H}{C}-\underset{H}{C}=\underset{H}{C}-\underset{H}{C}=\overset{+}{N}\diagup^{CH_3}_{\diagdown CH_3}$$

$$H_3C\diagdown \atop H_3C\diagup \overset{+}{N}=\underset{H}{C}-\underset{H}{C}=\underset{H}{C}-\underset{H}{C}=\underset{H}{C}-N\diagup^{CH_3}_{\diagdown CH_3}$$

(VI)

trons occupy the four lowest energy levels of the one-dimensional electron gas model. The electron distribution for the permitted discrete states is given by the solution of Eq. (79) with the proper limiting conditions for the first five quantum states ($n = 1, 2, 3, 4,$ and 5). Figures 31 and 32 will serve as illustrations.

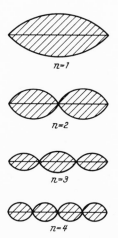

$n=1$

$n=2$

$n=3$

$n=4$

FIG. 31. Function of an electron in a one-dimensional box with $n = 1, 2, 3,$ and 4.

The number of nodes is $(n - 1)$ which increases with increasing quantum number. At the ends where $V = \infty$, there is also no vibration. The eight π electrons occupy the four lowest energy levels because only two electrons with opposite spin may be assigned to each state. The process of light absorption corresponds to the transition of an electron from a four-quantum, fully occupied, state to the five-quantum, unoccupied, state.

If an N atom is introduced into the middle of the chain, in lieu of a CH group, the electron gas suffers a disturbance which is caused by the

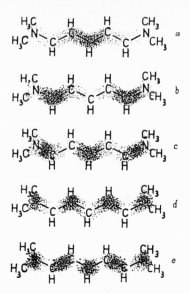

FIG. 32. Electron density distribution in a conjugated chain with $n = 1, 2, 3, 4,$ and 5.

greater electronegativity of the nitrogen in comparison with its neighboring atoms. The potential now can be indicated in an idealized way in Fig. 33.

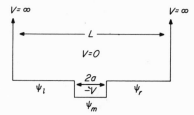

FIG. 33. Model of a one-dimensional electron box with a disturbance in the center.

In the center of the one-dimensional box, the potential assumes a negative value $-V$, for the distance $2a$. This distance corresponds to the efficient diameter of the nitrogen atom. This is in contrast with the course of the potential of the undisturbed chain where the value throughout is 0. The limiting conditions for the differential equation for this case are:

$$V_\infty \text{ for } 0 > s > L,$$
$$V_0 \text{ for } 0 < s < \tfrac{1}{2}L - a \text{ and } \tfrac{1}{2}L + a < s < L,$$
$$-V_1 \text{ for } \tfrac{1}{2}L - a < s < \tfrac{1}{2}L + a.$$

Upon integration of the differential equation we obtain:

$$\frac{d^2\psi}{ds^2} + \frac{8\pi^2 m}{h^2}(E - V_s)\psi = 0 \tag{76}$$

One must note that at the transition points of the CH groups to the N atom, the ψ_l, ψ_m, ψ_r functions as well as the differentials $d\psi_l/ds$, $d\psi_m/ds$, $d\psi_r/ds$ (steady-state condition) must be equal to each other. On the basis of these conditions of steadiness and normalization, where ψ^2 integrated over the total length L must be unity, one can obtain the energy eigenvalues. Energy differences $E_{n+1} - E_n$ represent the absorption maxima. For the case of the polymethene chain with a substituted N group, one can write the formula:

$$\frac{1}{\lambda_N} = \frac{1}{\lambda_{CH}} \pm \frac{4\nu_a}{h \cdot cL}. \tag{82}$$

The $+$ sign holds for an even number of double bonds and represents a shift of λ_{max} to the violet, whereas the minus sign holds for an uneven number and indicates a red shift.

Based on the illustrations of the vibrations (Figs. 34 and 35), one can

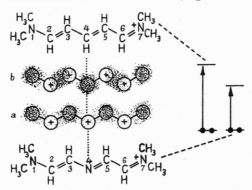

Fig. 34. Lowering of light absorption frequency if a CH group is replaced by N in an even-numbered chain.

obtain a qualitative picture of these shifts. If the N atom enters the chain in the middle and the chain has an odd number of C atoms, the 4-quantum ground state is not markedly changed by the greater electronegativity of the hydrogen atoms. However, the 5-quantum state has a vibration amplitude in the middle of the chain which indicates a greater electron density. The 5-quantum state, therefore, is preferred because of the electronegativity of the nitrogen atom and the transition from the $n = 4$ to $n = 5$ is facilitated. This in turn means a red shift of the first absorption maximum in the replacement of a CH_2 group by an N atom. If the number of C atoms in a chain is even, the middle of the chain in the ground state has a vibrational amplitude, i.e., a high probability for the presence of electrons. However, the first excited state shows a node. If the replacement is carried out

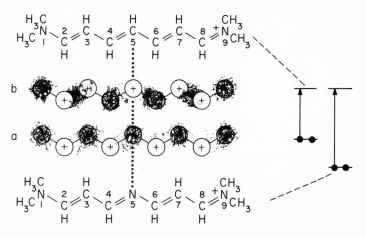

Fig. 35. Increase in light absorption frequency if a CH group is replaced by N in an odd-numbered chain.

there, the ground state is preferred over the excited state, and the electronic transition is made more difficult and requires a larger energy. This in turn means that the shift of the first absorption maximum must take place towards shorter wavelengths if a CH group is replaced by an N atom in a chain with an even number of carbon atoms. Analogous considerations can predict the direction in which the absorption maximum will be shifted if a nitrogen replaces a CH group at another position in the chain. The shift derived in the above equation amounts to about 1000 Å. The agreement of this result with experimental experiences may be demonstrated in several examples.[16] Symmetrical cyanine absorbs at 5240 Å, and the corresponding N compound at 4240 Å.

[16] H. Kuhn, *Helv. Chim. Acta* **34**, 2371 (1951); *Chimia (Switz.)* **4**, 203 (1950); **5**, 107 (1951); *Z. Elektrochem.* **55**, 220 (1951).

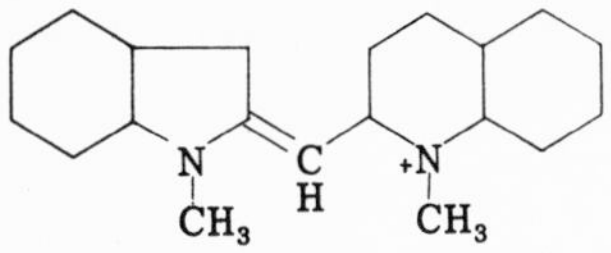

5240 Å 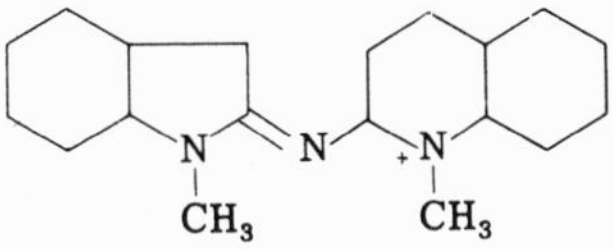   4240 Å

In the analogous sulfur compounds, the replacement of a CH group by N causes a shift from 4220 to 3680 Å. In both cases the number of conjugated double bonds is even. Hence the shift of the absorption maximum is towards shorter wavelengths in agreement with the above derivation. However, in dyestuffs with an uneven number of double bonds and the same replacement, the shift of the absorption goes towards the red as is shown in the example

$(CH_3)_2N$—⟨ ⟩—$\underset{H}{C}$=⟨ ⟩=$\overset{+}{N}(CH_3)_2$ ⟶ $(CH_3)_2N$—⟨ ⟩—N=⟨ ⟩=$\overset{+}{N}(CH_3)_2$

5030 Å — Michler's hydrol blue   7250 Å — Binschedler's green

The same regularities are found in the transition between methylene red (I) and methylene blue (II) as well as in the compounds in the acridine series (III–VI). In all of these cases the absorption maximum shift is of the order of 1000 Å.

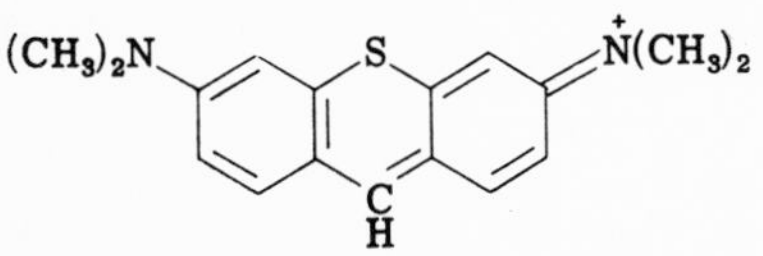

5645 Å   6680 Å

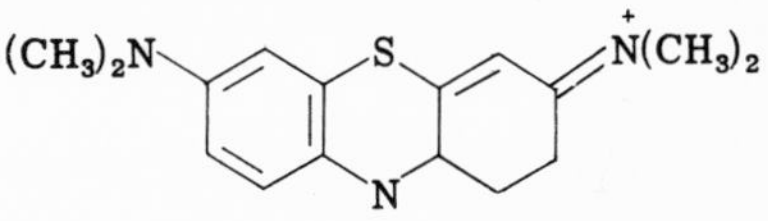

(I)   (II)

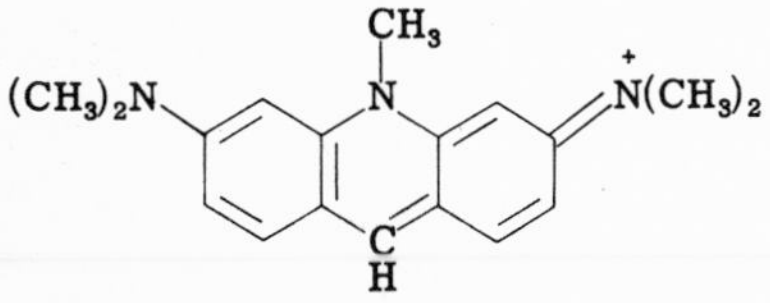

4910 Å   5645 Å

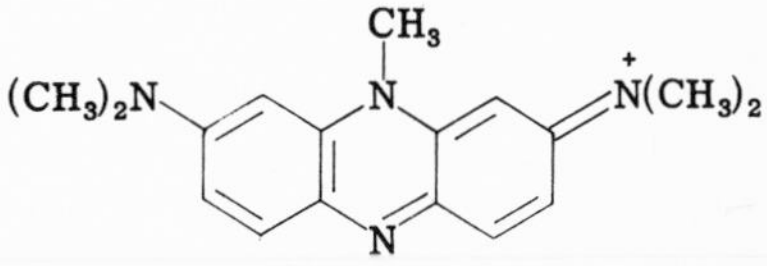

(III)   (IV)

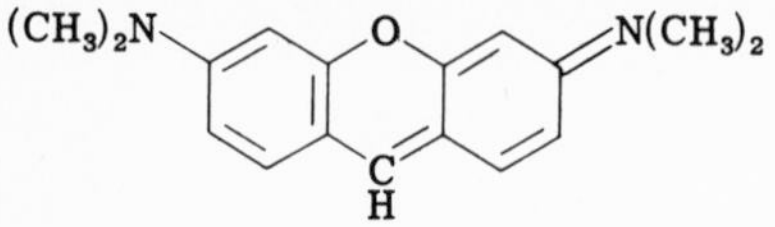

$(CH_3)_2N$ — O — $N(CH_3)_2$ structure with C—H bridge

5495 Å

(V)

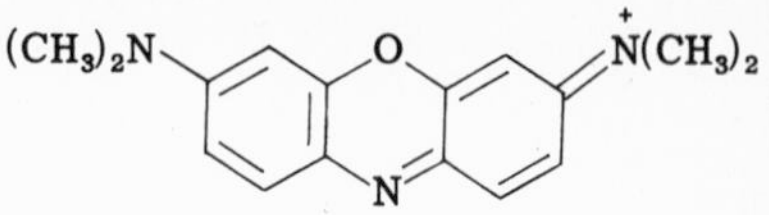

$(CH_3)_2N$ — O — $\overset{+}{N}(CH_3)_2$ structure with N bridge

6655 Å

(VI)

The quantitative treatment of the characteristic parameter for absorption processes, the absorption intensity, will not be discussed here. It involves the calculation of the transition probability of the electron from the ground state to the excited state. The reader is referred to the original papers.[17]

---

[17] E. A. Braude, *in* "Determination of Organic Structures by Physical Methods" (E. A. Braude and F. C. Nachod, eds.), Vol. I, p. 150. Academic Press, New York, 1955; cf. H. Kuhn, *Helv. Chim. Acta* **31,** 1441 (1948).

CHAPTER 21

Chemical Reactivity from the
Viewpoint of Electronic Theory

It is possible to survey the huge number of organic reactions and classify them into a few types, depending on whether electrons are donated or accepted among the reacting molecular species. One can differentiate between nonpolar, or radical, reactions where no electronic transition takes place, but where only neutral atom groups participate in the reaction, and polar reactions which are connected with a relative acceptance or donation of electrons among the reaction partners. The polar reactions are subdivided into two groups termed electrophilic and nucleophilic.

Although there are no sharp demarcations between these reaction types, and intermediary state reactions exist, these general characteristics are useful criteria for the respective categories. Typical of the polar ("cryptoionic") reactions[1] is their easy and frequent acid and base catalysis. Their rate is quite generally influenced by polar solvents. Yet light, oxygen, and peroxides have hardly any influence upon their rate. In general, polar reactions take place instantaneously, i.e., they show no induction period, and are mostly encountered in the liquid or dissolved state but rarely in the gas phase.

In contrast to this, the category of radical reactions generally has a more or less extended induction period followed by a chain reaction. Radical reactions are frequently influenced by light, oxygen, and peroxides. Many substances, known as inhibitors, which can produce a chain termination interfere with the course of radical reactions. This contrast to the polar reactions also extends to other criteria: radical reactions are hardly influenced by acids or bases and are not subject to the influence of polar solvents.

In order to understand the classification scheme for reactions, some

---

[1] H. Meerwein, *Ann.* **455**, 227 (1927).

new terms for the reacting atomic groups will be introduced. Reagents may be termed nucleophiles, electrophiles, and radicals. They are called nucleophilic when they are electron donors. By donating electrons they change into nuclei, or search out nuclei which will accept their electrons, partly or entirely. They are also named anionoid since they can produce anions. The most diverse groups will be found in this classification. The ammonia molecule NH_3 is a nucleophilic reagent, because it may react by partial surrender of its lone electron pair to a molecule with an electron gap such as BF_3 or $AlCl_3$. Metals such as Na, K, and Ca could be called nucleophilic reagents, on account of their ability to donate electrons. In an analogous fashion one might also consider the anions OH^- and CN^-.

It can be seen that nucleophilic reagents form a heterogeneous group of materials which can participate in chemical processes such as the oxidation of Sn^{++} to Sn^{4+}, the transition of a metal into the ionic state ($Na \rightarrow Na^+$), the neutralization of OH^- with NH_4^+ with formation of H_2O and NH_3, or the addition of NH_3 to BF_3 with complex formation. All these processes have a common denominator, namely, the surrender of one electron or the sharing of electrons with an electron acceptor.

Similarly, one terms electrophilic reagents such atom groups which accept electrons completely or in part from other atoms or atom groups. They may also add to electron rich positions (lone electron pairs) and thus participate in sharing electrons of the donor molecule. Electrophilic reagents then are groups such as NO_3^-, SO_3^-, RCO^+, $AlCl_3$, BF_3, etc.

Finally, there are radicals, i.e., atoms or atom groups, which do not change the number of electrons in a chemical reaction.

In the same fashion, reactions are subdivided into nucleophilic and electrophilic reactions. In a reaction one distinguishes between a substrate and a reagent. But this distinction is quite conventional and not always feasible. There has been some agreement to transfer the name of the reagent to the total reaction. Thus a substitution has been termed a nucleophilic substitution if the reagent has a nucleophilic nature. Addition of CH_3I to $(CH_3)_3N$ under formation of a quaternary ammonium salt is a nucleophilic substitution since $(CH_3)_3N$ is considered the reagent.

$$CH_3I + (CH_3)_3N \rightarrow (CH_3)_4N^+ + I^-.$$

On the other hand, if the reagent is an electrophilic substance, the total reaction course is termed electrophilic. For example, nitration of benzene is an electrophilic substitution because NO_2^+, the reagent, is electrophilic:

$$NO_2^+ + C_6H_5H \rightarrow C_6H_5NO_2 + H^+.$$

A series of nucleophilic and electrophilic substitution reactions is summarized in Table 28.

TABLE 28

Electrophilic substitutions
$C_6H_5H + NO_2^+ \rightarrow C_6H_5NO_2 + H^+$
$(CH_3)_2NH + NO_2^+ \rightarrow (CH_3)_2N{-}NO_2 + H^+$
$C_6H_5OH + RCO^+ \rightarrow C_6H_5O{-}COCH_3 + H^+$
$C_6H_5H + Cl^+ \rightarrow C_6H_5Cl + H^+$
$C_6H_5N_2^+ + CH_3OH \rightarrow CH_3ON_2 + C_6H_5 + H^+$

Nucleophilic substitutions
$C_2H_5Br + CN^- \rightarrow C_2H_5CN + Br^-$
$C_2H_5I + (C_2H_5)_2S \rightarrow (C_2H_5)_3S^+ + I^-$
$(C_2H_5)_3N + C_2H_5I \rightarrow (C_2H_5)_4N^+ + I^-$
$(R_3S)^+ + NR_3 \rightarrow R_4N^+ + R_2S$
$R_4N^+ + OH^- \rightarrow ROH + R_3N$
$C_2H_5O^- + C_2H_5Cl \rightarrow (C_2H_5)_2O + Cl^-$

The position of the substrate, which will be attacked by the nucleophilic or electrophilic reagent, respectively, is determined by the relative electron density in the molecule. This is best demonstrated in molecular diagrams where the degree of bonding and the relative electric charge distribution, i.e., charge density and free valence, are taken into account. These parameters are characteristic of the three types of chemical reactions. Addition reactions are determined by bond order, substitution reactions by electron density, and radical reactions by free valence.

Both VB as well as MO theory permit one to construct molecular diagrams, in which the characteristic parameters for the structure of the molecules can be incorporated. The calculated bond order, the free valence from one atom, and the charge density in the neighborhood of the various atoms can be properly indicated.

Using the VB method, one calculates the bond order which, in general, is not a whole number but contains weighted contributions of the canonical structures present in the resonance hybrids. The per cent double bond character is obtained by calculating the total weight of all structures in which the C—C bond is present as a double bond. In the case of benzene there is one Kekulé and one Dewar structure, with 39 and 7%, respectively, represented in the resonance hybrid. Consequently, each C—C bond in benzene after the delocalization of the π electrons has 46% double bond character. The total bond order which arises from the combined σ and π

electrons is 1.46. From this amount 1.00 is contributed by the σ bond and 0.46 by the π bond. In the case of naphthalene, one must take into account 42 structures where the single contributing weights determine the final result.

The calculation of bond order according to the MO method is somewhat more complicated. First, the bond order, $p_{r,s}$ between two C atoms, r and s, related to the mobile π electrons is obtained by feeding the partial bond order of each orbital as a product with the coefficients c_1, c_2, . . . or the corresponding atomic orbitals ψ_1, ψ_2, . . . in a linear combination into Eq. (52). Then the partial bond orders of all molecular orbitals are summed up, whereby one must take into account that each MO has two occupying electrons. This may be expressed by:

$$p_{r,s} = \sum_{j} n_j c_{rj} c_{sj},$$

where c_{rj} and c_{sj} are the coefficients of the jth molecular orbital, and n_j stands for the number of π-electrons which occupy it. In this fashion, one calculates for benzene the bond order of 0.667 owing to equalization of the six participating π electrons, and therefore the total bond order between two C—C atoms is 1.667.

The maximum number of electrons which the free carbon atom can accept is calculated as:[2]

$$N_{max} = 3 + \sqrt{3} = 4.732.$$

If the bond order is subtracted from this maximum number, a number results which is a measure of the free valence extending from each atom. In the diagram (I) the total bond orders between adjacent carbon atoms is

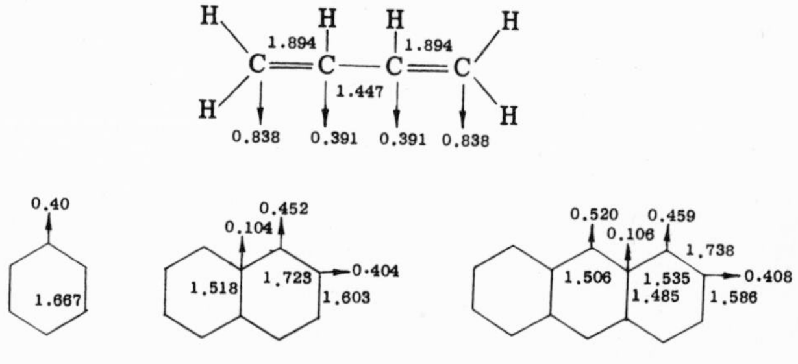

(I)

---

[2] For the derivation of this equation cf. W. E. Moffit, *Trans. Faraday Soc.* **45**, 373 (1949); cf. E. Hückel, *Z. Elektrochem.* **61**, 883 (1957).

shown. The arrows indicate free valences as obtained from the MO method. Both methods furnish different numerical results. However, they yield corresponding gradations within each molecule.

The diagram of butadiene shows that the three bonds between the carbon atoms are largely equalized and that free valences appear at the C_1 and C_4 atoms to the amount of 0.838. This explains the well known 1,4-addition of bromine to butadiene and the rearrangement of the double bond into the 2,3-position according to:

$$Br_2 + H_2C=C-C=CH_2 \longrightarrow H_2C-C=C-CH_2$$

The diagram for naphthalene shows that the bond order between the α and β positions is the largest, whereas the free valency had its maximum valency in the α position. In anthracene it is the 9-position of the molecule which is endowed with the largest free valence number. Therefore this position is the most reactive one in addition reactions.

The charge distribution in the molecule is also shown in molecular diagrams and permits one to predict the place of attack for anions or cations respectively, even though forces of nonelectrostatic nature may occur in the activated complex. According to the MO method, the free charge on a given atom r is defined by the equation:

$$q_r = \sum_{i=1}^{l} n_i(c_r{}^i)^2 \tag{82a}$$

as the sum of the squares of the coefficients of the AO's which form the ψ_1 function, where the occupation number of the individual orbitals is 0, 1, or 2 electrons.[3] The same equation holds under the assumption that the AO functions are orthogonal to each other, i.e., that their overlap integral S has the value of zero. It can be shown that a charge q in an atom r is equal to the change of the total energy of the molecule E by the Coulomb integral of the corresponding atom Q_r:

$$q_r = \frac{\partial E}{\partial Q_r}. \tag{82b}$$

Similarly, the bond order p_{rs} between two atoms r and s can be derived so that it is equal to the change of total energy E divided by the resonance integral β_{rs} between the two atoms r and s:

---

[3] B. H. Chirgwin and C. A. Coulson, *Proc. Roy. Soc.* **A201**, 197 (1950).

$$p_{rs} = \frac{1}{2}\frac{\partial E}{\partial \beta_{rs}}. \qquad (82c)$$

The charge distribution of a number of molecules is shown below (II).

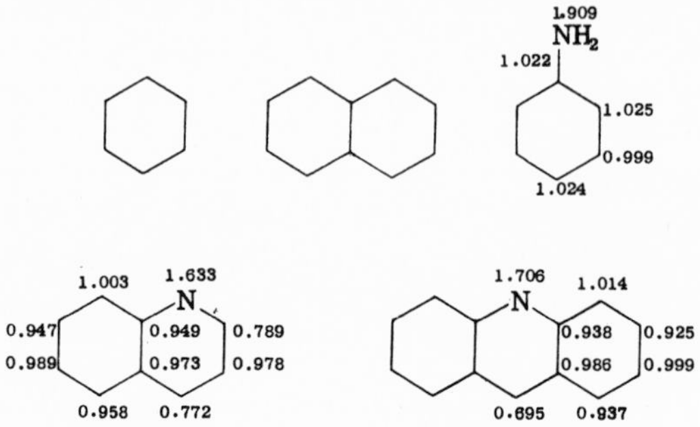

Quinoline   Acridine

(II)

The benzene molecule shows a regular charge distribution. The diagram for aniline shows that an electron shift has taken place from the amino group to the phenyl ring in such a way that the o- and p-positions are more negatively charged in contrast to the m-position. We shall see that this charge distribution accounts for the o-p directing action of the amino group in electrophilic substitutions. Analogous statements can be made for the charge distribution in quinoline and acridine. If a CH group in naphthalene or anthracene, respectively, is replaced by nitrogen, the symmetric charge distribution is canceled as can be seen in the molecular diagrams. It is interesting to note that the decrease of basicity of the nitrogen in the series aniline, diphenylamine, triphenylamine can be followed by studying the respective charge distributions. The charge of a lone electron

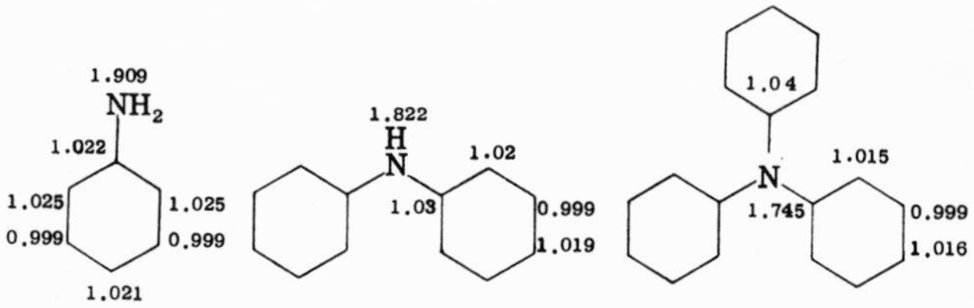

(III)

pair on the nitrogen atoms in the series (III) is distributed increasingly over the phenyl rings. Triphenylamine has the ability to form salts which would require addition of a proton to the lone electron pair.

It was stated above that certain special positions in the molecular diagram *may* serve as centers of attack of electrophilic or nucleophilic reagents, respectively, but that they *must not* be responsible for the ensuing end product. The reason for this lies in the fact that substances reacting with each other must necessarily go through a so-called "transition state"[4] in which rearrangement and changes in grouping may take place, leading to the formation of the activated complex. The way in which this transition state arises and how resonance phenomena contribute to its relative stabilization may be demonstrated in the reaction:

$$Br^- + CH_3Br \rightarrow BrCH_3 + Br^-$$

If one ascribes the role of reagent to Br^-, and the role of substrate to CH_3Br, the above reaction must be a nucleophilic substitution since Br^- is nucleophilic. Since the states at the beginning and at the end are chemically identical, this reaction can only be followed in using radioactive Br^- isotope, and measuring its incorporation in the organic portion, CH_3Br. Alternatively, one can employ an asymmetric, optically active, trisubstituted alkyl group such as

$$\underset{}{\overset{H}{\diagdown}}\ \underset{}{\overset{CH_3}{\diagup}}$$
C
$$\diagup\ \diagdown_{C_2H_5}$$

and measure the time dependence of optical activity. As will be shown below, racemization must take place as the reaction goes through the transition state.

In a combination of both methods, the racemization of optically active-2-octyl iodide with radioactive iodine has been followed.[5] It was found that for each iodine incorporated in the organic molecule, a molecule of active octyl iodide is reacemized. These facts can only be reconciled if the attack

[4] H. Pelzer and E. Wigner, *Z. physik. Chem.* **B15,** 445 (1932); H. Eyring, *J. Chem. Phys.* **3,** 107 (1935); M. G. Evans and M. Polanyi, *Trans. Faraday Soc.* **31,** 875 (1935).

[5] E. D. Hughes, F. Juliusburger, S. Masterman, B. Topley, and J. Weiss, *J. Chem. Soc.* p. 1525 (1935).

of the nucleophilic reagent takes place from the opposite side of the halide according to the scheme:

$$I^- + \underset{H}{\overset{H}{\diagdown}}C{-}I \rightarrow \left[I^{-}\cdots \underset{H}{\overset{H}{\diagdown}}C\cdots I \longleftrightarrow I\cdots \underset{H}{\overset{H}{\diagdown}}C\cdots I^{-} \right] \rightarrow I{-}CH_3 + I^-$$

Activated complex

In the transition state of the activated complex, the two iodine atoms are at the same distance from the carbon atom. In the transition state both iodines have become equivalent, and the charge can jump from one to the other. This permits the introduction of a resonance process which stabilizes the complex by liberating resonance energy. The stabilization energy acts in the direction which lessens the activation energy required for the reaction.

In Fig. 36 the reaction scheme is shown for the change in energy con-

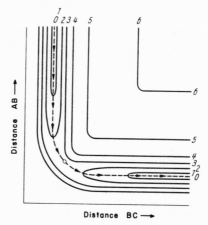

FIG. 36. Saddle plane of the potential energy values in the reaction AB + C → A + BC.

tent of an AB molecule being approached by a C atom, as well as of the BC molecule being approached by an A atom. The axes show the AB and BC distances which are changed by the approach of the C or A atom, respectively. The energy curves could be considered as the contour lines of a mountain system with the plane of the paper as the base. They are symmetrical with respect to the plane which halves the angle between the axes. If one starts with the BC molecule and A an infinite distance away, one finds a zero energy line at the upper left portion of the diagram. As the A atom approaches the BC molecule, the BC distance is increased and the energy contour lines of 2 and 3 are surpassed. Then one follows a path along the dotted curve to a saddle point, indicated by a small open circle, afterwards descending again symmetrically and arriving at a zero energy line at the lower right corner, corresponding to the AB molecule with C moving towards infinity.

In this fashion the change of the BC molecule to AB took place with the smallest possible expense of activation energy. This was accomplished by a resonance stabilization of the (activated) transition complex (A . . . B . . . C) in which the distances between AC and BC became equal. This point is the small open circle in the diagram (Fig. 36) and is situated at a relative minimum in the potential mountain range.

The above kind of nucleophilic substitution is a reaction of the second order, since it is proportional to the [I^-], as well as to the [CH_3Br] concentration. It is symbolized by the abbreviation S_{N2} (nucleophilic substitution, second order) and is accompanied by a stereochemical inversion of the molecule as can be shown in a large number of examples. One might cite the racemization of *sec.* butanol, menthol, α-phenylethylalcohol, methylcyclohexanol, etc., in the presence of strong bases, i.e., nucleophilic reagents.

Some interesting regularities are observed in the homologous series of alkyl halides. The rate constant k_0 of the S_{N2} reaction decreases with increasing chain length, for which, at first, one might believe that sterical reasons are responsible. The longer the chain length, the smaller is the probability that collision takes place at the position which would lead to reaction. Simultaneously, one notes an increase in activation energy which can be explained as decrease of hyperconjugation, owing to the increasing distance of the CH_3 group from the reaction site. If the reaction of alkyl halides is carried out in solvents which act as weak bases (water, alcohol, etc.) the reaction type changes from S_{N2} to S_{N1}.[5a] It becomes a first order reaction since it now only depends on the concentration of the alkyl halides. The solvent is present in a large excess, and hence its concentration during the reaction can be considered constant. The reaction is monomolecular, or better pseudo-monomolecular, because the solvent plays an important role. This is termed solvolysis.

If one considers the addition of hydrogen halides in general as proton-

---

[5a] For reaction types and examples, cf. E. S. Gould "Mechanism and Structure in Organic Chemistry," pp. 457, 463, 473, and 478. Holt, New York, 1959.

donating HX compounds to a non-symmetrical olefin, one observes regularities which had already been noted by Markownikoff[6] and which have been summarized in the Markownikoff rule. According to this rule, the addition of HX to an olefin always takes place in such a fashion that the H atom seeks the carbon having the largest number of hydrogen atoms. The addition of HBr to propylene, for example, does not lead to n-propyl bromide but to isopropyl bromide according to the scheme:

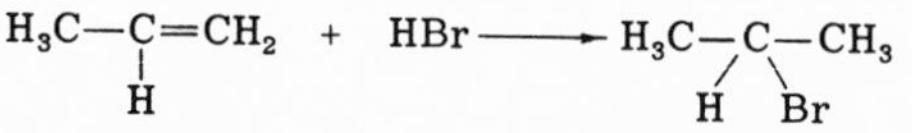

$$H_3C-\underset{\underset{H}{|}}{C}=CH_2 \ + \ HBr \longrightarrow H_3C-\underset{\overset{/}{H}\ \ \overset{\backslash}{Br}}{C}-CH_3$$

This regularity can be explained on the basis of electron shift effects. The methyl group is an electron donor, so that propylene has a polarity as shown below:

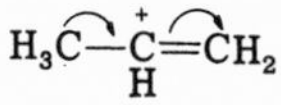

$$H_3\overset{\frown}{C}-\underset{H}{\overset{+}{C}}\overset{\frown}{=}CH_2$$

$$(1) \ \ (2) \ \ (3)$$

The C_3 atom appears more negative than the C_2 atom. The electrophilic portion of the compound HX (in the case of HBr the H^+ ion) will tend to add to the more negative C_3 atom, and the nucleophilic portion Br^-, in turn, will tend towards the C_2 atom.

If one considers the addition of HCl to vinyl chloride

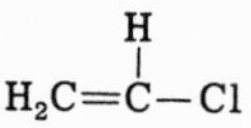

$$H_2C=\underset{\overset{|}{Cl}}{\overset{H}{C}}-Cl$$

one is at first surprised that chlorine adjoins the same C atom which already carries a chlorine atom. One would think, rather, that owing to repulsion of two like atoms, addition of the second chlorine would take place at the more remote C atom, leading to a symmetrical dichloroethane. This, however, is not the case and the asymmetrical 1,1-dichloroethane

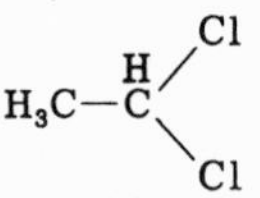

$$H_3C-\underset{}{\overset{H}{C}}\overset{\overset{\textstyle Cl}{\diagup}}{\underset{\diagdown}{\ }}_{Cl}$$

is formed. Its formation is explained by an induction effect of the halogen atom. It takes electrons from the neighboring C atom and acquires a

---

[6] W. Markownikoff, *Ann.* **153,** 256 (1870).

positive charge, which in turn becomes the site for the addition of the nucleophilic Cl^-:

$$H_2C=\overset{\overset{\textstyle H}{|}}{C}-Cl \longrightarrow H_2C=\underset{+}{\overset{\overset{\textstyle H}{|}}{C}}=\underset{-}{Cl} \;+\; HCl \longrightarrow H_3C-\overset{\overset{\textstyle H}{|}}{C}\overset{\textstyle Cl}{\underset{\textstyle Cl}{\diagdown}}$$

Whenever deviations of this rule were observed, it was possible to show that one was dealing with a different reaction mechanism, where other factors became the determining ones for the reaction. In the presence of oxygen or peroxides, halogen addition does not follow Markownikoff's rule. In this case, it takes place at the carbon having the most hydrogens and the normal bromide is formed. The reaction mechanism in this case is quite different. Through the action of oxygen or peroxide on HBr, atomic bromine is formed:

$$HBr + O_2 \rightarrow (HO_2) + Br$$

which attacks, in the general manner of radicals, the location of the highest free valence. In the case of propylene, this is carbon atom 3:

$$CH_3-CH=CH_2 + Br \rightarrow CH_3\overset{.}{C}H-CH_2Br.$$

The intermediary free radical reacts with HBr, forming new Br atoms:

$$CH_3-\overset{\overset{\textstyle H}{|}}{C}-CH_2Br + HBr \rightarrow CH_3-CH_2-CH_2Br + Br$$

which again react with propylene. A chain reaction ensues, and the chain is only broken when two Br atoms combine to form a Br_2 molecule.

Vinyl chloride

$$CH_2=CHCl$$

combines with acids in the presence of oxygen or peroxides with the formation of the symmetrical dihalide and the same is encountered in the addition of the mercaptan, C_6H_5SH:

$$CH_3-\underset{\underset{\textstyle H}{|}}{C}=CH_2 + C_6H_5SH \overset{O_2}{\rightarrow} CH_3-CH_2-CH_2-S-C_6H_5.$$

However, changing the course of the addition of HCl and HI in the presence of O_2 or peroxides, respectively, is not possible. It always takes place according to the Markownikoff rule.

If the attacking reagent is electrophilic, the total reaction is called an electrophilic reaction or, more specifically, an electrophilic substitution. One atom or atomic group of a substrate is exchanged with the attacking reagent. It is denoted by the symbol S_{E1} or S_{E2}, respectively, depending on whether the electrophilic substitution is first or second order.

An example of an electrophilic substitution is the nitration of aromatic hydrocarbons with concentrated nitric acid. The attacking reagent is the nitronium ion:

$$HONO_2 \rightleftarrows NO_2^+ + OH^-,$$

and nitration can be formulated as:

$$C_6H_5H + NO_2^+ \rightarrow C_6H_5NO_2 + H^+.$$

Chlorination of benzene with hypochlorous acid, HOCl, also takes place as an electrophilic substitution, if it is carried out in strongly acid solution.

$$C_6H_5H + \overset{-}{H}O\overset{+}{Cl} \rightarrow C_6H_5Cl + \overset{+}{H}\overset{-}{O}H.$$

In contrast to saturated hydrocarbons which have only σ bonds and therefore rarely undergo polar reactions, the aromatic hydrocarbons, owing to the greater mobility of the electrons, undergo electrophilic reactions with great facility. Chlorination of benzene with gaseous Cl_2 in the presence of $FeCl_3$ as catalyst is an electrophilic substitution, in contrast to the chlorination of paraffins at high temperatures which requires the presence of Cl atoms. Consequently, it is a nonpolar radical reaction. The same holds for nitration of paraffins.

One frequently encounters reactions which change their character depending on external conditions. Bromination of naphthalene at temperatures below 400° is mainly an electrophilic substitution which takes place at the heterogeneous surface of the catalyst. At higher temperatures, however, it becomes a homolytic reaction, because thermally created bromine atoms become the attacking reagent and interact as radicals with the substrate. Other reaction conditions which may lead to the formation of free halogen atoms, such as the interaction of light, may initiate a radical mechanism.

The reaction schemes shown below refer to additional electrophilic substitutions among which the Friedel-Crafts reaction and the coupling with diazonium ions deserves special mention.

$$C_6H_5H + SO_3 = C_6H_5SO_3^- + H^+$$
$$C_6H_5H + Cl\!\!-\!\!SO_3H = C_6H_6SO_3^- + H^+ + HCl$$
$$C_6H_5H + CH_3CO^+ = C_5H_6COCH_3 + H^+$$
$$C_6H_5H + CH_3COCl + AlCl_3 = C_6H_5COCH_3 + H^+ + AlCl_4^-$$
$$RC_6H_4H + C_6H_5N_2^+ = RC_6H_4N\!\!=\!\!NC_6H_5 + H^+.$$

Addition reactions to a double or triple bond may be nucleophilic as well as electrophilic. The latter reaction type is the more common one and takes place in the presence of polar reagents. In contrast to this, the addition of a halogen to a double bond in the gas phase, or a photosensitized reaction always requires free radicals.

There are reasons for assuming[7] that the polar addition of a halogen to a double bond takes place via the halogen cation as the rate-determining step:

$$CH_2\!\!=\!\!CH_2 + \overset{+}{Br}\!\!-\!\!\overset{-}{Br} \rightarrow CH_2\!\!-\!\!CH_2 + \overset{-}{Br}$$
$$\underset{\underset{+}{Br}}{}$$

If the addition of the halogen is carried out in the presence of Cl^- or NO_3^- ions, respectively, a dibromide results, in addition to the products $BrCH_2\!\!-\!\!CH_2Cl$ and $BrCH_2\!\!-\!\!CH_2\!\!-\!\!ONO_2$. Both byproducts can only be explained by assuming an intermediary formation of carbonium ions C^+ so that the addition of the halogen atoms does not take place simultaneously. One could term the above reaction mechanism an electrophilic addition, because the primary addition of electrophilic Br^+ determines the total reaction rate.

Similarly, the addition of H_2O, H_2SO_4, HCl, $NOCl$, etc. to a double bond must occur as an electrophilic reaction, which has been termed Ad_E. Meerwein[8] was the first to stipulate carbonium ions in the rearrangements in the camphor series. This was extended to the concept of "cryptoionic" reactions. Their intermediary appearance has been proved in numerous recent studies.[9]

In contrast, the addition of ammonia to an aldehyde is a nucleophilic addition reaction (symbol Ad_N) which takes place according to the scheme:

[7] See the comprehensive papers of E. D. Hughes, *Trans. Faraday Soc.* **37**, 603 (1941); V. Franzen and H. Krauch, *Chem. Ztg.* **79**, 243 (1955); W. von E. Doering and T. C. Aschner, *J. Am. Chem. Soc.* **75**, 393 (1953).

[8] H. Meerwein, *Ber.* **55**, 2500 (1922); *Ann.* **455**, 227 (1927).

[9] H. Meerwein et al., *Z. angew. Chem.* **67**, 374 (1955).

$$R-\overset{H}{\underset{H}{C}}=O \quad + \quad \overset{H}{\underset{H}{:NH}} \longrightarrow R-\overset{NH_2}{\underset{H}{C}}-OH$$

Because of the electronegativity of the oxygen, a charge shift takes place from the carbon to the oxygen, so that the former appears positively charged. The nucleophilic ammonia molecule joins, with its lone electron pair of the nitrogen, to the carbon atom, while a proton migrates to the negatively charged oxygen atom.

Nucleophilic addition reactions take place preferentially if a negatively charged carbanion can be formed. This is parallel to electrophilic additions where a positive carbonium ion is postulated. The addition of alcohols to α,β-unsaturated carbonyl compounds is an example of such a nucleophilic addition with intermediary formation of a carbanion, according to:

$$CH_3O^- \;+\; H_2C{=}\underset{H}{\overset{}{C}}{-}\underset{H}{\overset{}{C}}{=}O \;+\; H^+ \longrightarrow CH_3OCH_2{-}\overset{-}{CH}{-}CH{=}O \;+\; H^+$$

$$\longrightarrow CH_3OCH_2\,CH_2\overset{H}{C}{=}O$$

This formulation explains the addition of the electronegative portion CH_3O^- to the β position, which is verified experimentally. Polymerization reactions of olefins in the presence of $NaNH_2$ belong to the same category. In the first step a carbanion is formed:

$$\overset{-}{N}H_2 + CH_2{=}\overset{H}{C}{-}C_6H_5 \rightarrow NH_2{-}CH_2{-}CH{-}\overset{-}{CH}{-}C_6H_5$$

which can add to other olefin molecules according to:

$$NH_2{-}CH_2{-}\overset{-}{CH}{-}C_6H_5 + C_6H_5CH{=}CH_2 \rightarrow NH_2{-}CH_2{-}CH{-}CH_2{-}\overset{-}{CH}{-}C_6H_5 \ldots$$
$$\underset{C_6H_5}{|}$$

so that long chain reaction products results.[10] Elimination reactions, where olefins are formed while HX is split off, also belong to the family of nucleophilic reactions. An example of this type of reaction, symbolized with E_N, is the formation of propylene from isopropylbromide and sodium alcoholate:

$$C_2H_5ONa + (CH_3)_2\underset{Br}{\overset{H}{C}} \rightarrow C_2H_5OH + CH_3{-}CH{=}CH_2 + NaBr,$$

---

[10] W. C. F. Higginson and N. S. Wooding, *J. Chem. Soc.* **760**, 1178.

or the elimination of HBr from iso-butylbromide in the presence of water.

$$H_2O + (CH_3)_3CBr \rightarrow H_3O^+ + (CH_3)_2C{=}CH_2 + \overset{-}{Br}$$

The resulting double bond need not occur between two C atoms, but can also be situated between heteroatoms. This leads to a reversal of the reaction. The aldol condensation or the reversal of the Michael reaction are good examples of this type.

The regularities which are observed in the introduction of substituents into the benzene ring can be related to the charge distribution in the benzene molecule. They can be explained readily on the basis of electronic theory. The classical investigations of Holleman (1910) have shown that the substituents may be divided into two classes depending on their direction action.[11] Substituents of the first order direct a second group towards the o- and p-positions, whereas substituents of the second kind preferentially activate the benzene molecule in the m-position. Consideration of Table 29, in which o-, p-, and m-directing substituents are summarized, shows that the first group contains electron donors, whereas the second comprises elements and groups belonging to electron acceptors.

TABLE 29

Electrophilic Substitutions

Class I.	Class II.
Substituents directing mainly towards o-, p -position	Substituents directing mainly towards m-position
— Cl	— NO₂
—Br	— CO
— I	$-\overset{H}{C}{=}O$
— CH₃, — C₂H₅	$-\overset{O}{\overset{\|}{C}}-OH, \quad -\overset{O}{\overset{\|}{C}}-OR$
— OH, — OCH₃	$-\overset{O}{\overset{\|}{C}}-NH_2$
— NH₂	— SO₃H, CN
	+N(CH₃)₃

[11] Cf. comprehensive article by L. N. Ferguson, *Chem. Revs.* **50**, 47 (1952).

The donor action of the substituents does not influence the various positions in the benzene ring in the same manner. The molecular diagram of aniline (IV), for example, shows that the electron density in the o- and p-positions is higher compared to the m-position. The charge distribution shows an alternating course which can be explained on quantum mechanical grounds.[12] If aniline reacts with an electrophilic reagent such as, e.g., the

$$NH_2$$

1.03   1.03
1.00   1.00
1.04

(IV)

NO_2^+ ion present in a nitration process, the o- and p-positions are attacked since they are electronegative, and o- and p-derivatives are formed. If a substituent of the second kind, an electron acceptor, is present in the benzene molecule, the same o- and p-positions are mostly affected, yet now in the reverse sense. They are poorer with respect to negative charge, so that they appear positively charged towards the m-position. An electrophilic reagent therefore is directed to the m-position and retained there. The electron flux, or electron removal, respectively, at the o- and p-positions is seen from the alternating charge distribution in the molecule. Aside from the wave mechanical derivation, this can be explained by visualizing the valence structures. A charge distribution in the benzene molecule may take place with the formation of o- and p-quinoid structures respectively:

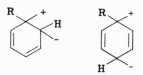

Yet formation of a *meta*-quinoid structure is not possible on the grounds of valence. However, it must be emphasized that substitution takes place at all three positions in the benzene molecule, so that only relative differences in reaction rate appear at the o-, p-, and m-positions, respectively.

---

[12] C. A. Coulson and H. C. Longuet-Higgins, *Proc. Roy. Soc.* **A191**, 39 (1947); **A192**, 16 (1948); **A193**, 447 (1948); R. G. Parr and R. S. Mulliken, *J. Chem. Phys.* **18**, 1338 (1950); H. H. Jaffé, *ibid.* **20**, 280 (1952).

The correctness of the above explanation of the substitution rules of benzene can be followed experimentally step by step. In the phenyltrimethylammonium ion, the positive $(CH_3)_3N^+$ ion, as an electron acceptor, directs an electrophilic reagent into the m-position. Hence, nitration furnishes the *meta* derivatives in 100% yields. However, if a CH_2 group is inserted between the phenyl ring and the $(CH_3)_3N^+$ ion, the percentage of m-derivatives decreases to 88% and simultaneously 12% of o- and p-nitro derivatives are formed. A further removal of the m-directing $(CH_3)_3N^+$ group from the phenyl ring through several CH_2 groups brings about a further decrease of the m-percentage and an increase in the yield of o- and p-derivatives, so that the chain $CH_2CH_2CH_2N^+(CH_3)_3$ now has become an o-, p-directing group. With increasing chain length, it gradually assumes the properties of the CH_3 group in toluene which as an electron donor is o-p-directing.

In an analogous fashion, an o-p-directing substituent may be changed to an m-directing one by changing its electronic arrangement. The CH_3 group in toluene, owing to the hyperconjugation effect, is a donor group, and directs an electrophilic reagent into the o- and p-positions. If one replaces the H atoms successively with electronegative Cl, the proportion of m-derivatives changes at the expense of the o- and p-derivatives. Trichloromethylbenzene is nitrated 64% in the m-position.

It has been noted that substituents of the first order increase the reaction rate compared with benzene, whereas substituents of the second order lower it. The numbers shown at the structures of toluene and ethyl benzoate below, respectively, show the ratio of nitration rates of the respective molecules compared with the nitration rate of benzene. In a similar fashion

one can also visualize the o-, p-, and m-directing action of the two substituents respectively.

Accurate measurements indicate that o- and p-positions are not equivalent as had been assumed up to now. The inductive effect of a substituent upon the charge distribution in the phenyl ring is stronger for the two neighboring o-positions than for the p-position. This occurs as a result of the shorter distance of the o-position from the inducing substituent. In contrast, the conjugation effect of the p-position is stronger than that of the o-position. From a valence structure viewpoint, this is connected with the greater stability of the p-quinoid structures in contrast with the o-quinoid. In the parlance of the VB theory, this means that the p-quinoid structure (V) has a greater contribution in the resonance hybrid than the o-quinoid polar structure (VI).

(V)   (VI)

The difference in the weights arises because in the creation of an o-quinoid structure one double bond must be delocalized, but in the creation of a p-quinoid formula two double bonds are involved.

The antagonism between inductive and mesomeric effects can be followed very well in studying the ratios of o/p yields. In the series C_6H_5F, C_6H_5Cl, C_6H_5Br, and C_6H_5I, the o/p ratio of the mononitro derivative increases from a value of 1/8 to a value of almost 1. This series is the same as the series of decreasing electronegativity and increasing conjugation effect of the halogens. It should be noted that the more voluminous iodine group does not interfere with the entry of the NO_2 group in the o-position. This effect is encountered with other groups. The steric influence of already present substituents can be demonstrated by comparing nitration yields of o- and p-derivatives in the series:

The yield of o-nitro derivatives decreases in the above series, whereas it correspondingly increases for p-derivatives. The ratio o/p changes from values of 1.4 to 0.15 in the direction of increasing volume of the side chain.

It is not always simple to predict the position which will be occupied by a newly introduced atomic group if more than one substituent is already present in the phenyl ring. The m-nitroanisole molecule, as well as m-nitrobenzaldehyde, is nitrated in the 2-position against all expectations. Similar irregularities are noted if two different halogen atoms are present in the benzene ring. A very subtle gradation of ± inductive and ± mesomeric effects will determine the final charge distribution in the molecule which is responsible for the directing action.

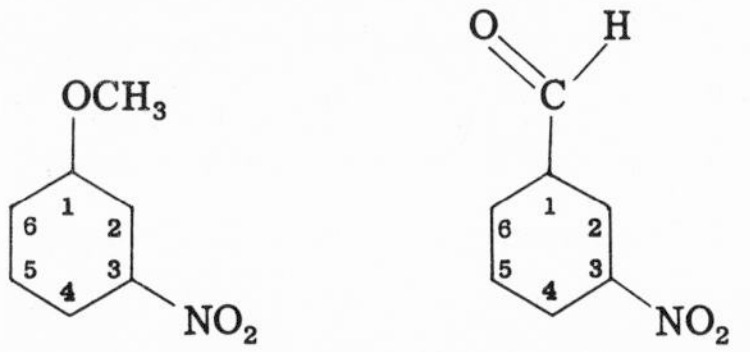

If the phenyl ring becomes electron-poor by the introduction of strong electron acceptors, such as NO_2 groups, it must exhibit positions which strongly attract nucleophilic reagents. The 1-bromo-2,4-dinitrobenzene readily exchanges the bromine atom against a methoxy group according to the nucleophilic reaction scheme:

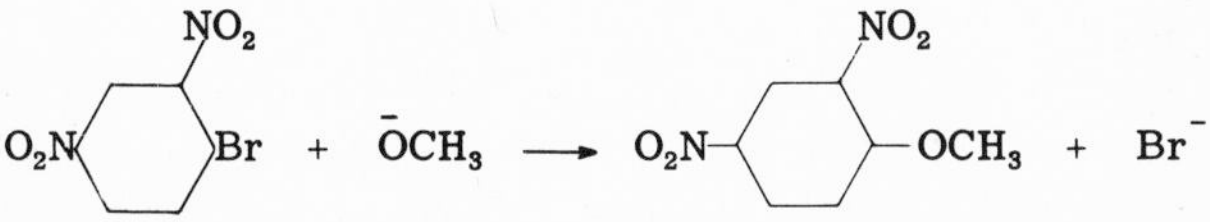

For nucleophilic aromatic substitutions, the directing action of the substituents must be opposite in direction to the above electrophilic nitration reaction. As an example, the reader is referred to a reaction which has been studied a great deal. It consists of the introduction of a halogen ion into the benzene ring by decomposition of the corresponding diazonium salts. It is represented by the scheme:

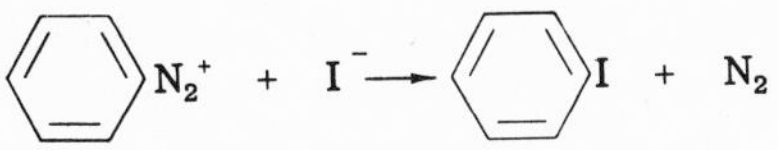

which is an S_{N1} reaction, a nucleophilic substitution of the first order. The course of the reaction is monomolecular, because the decomposition of the diazonium ion

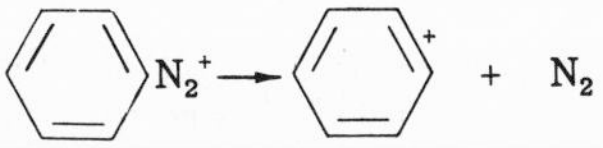

probably only depends upon the diazonium ion concentration. It is the slowest reaction step and hence rate determining. The subsequent union of the positive phenyl ion with the halogen ion is immeasurably rapid:

The influence of various groups in the m-position upon the decomposition of these diazonium salts has been investigated.[13] It was found that groups which have a strong $+M$ effect, i.e., which donate charges to the phenyl ring conjugatively, increase the decomposition of the diazonium ion up to tenfold. This means that the m-position is activated in a nucleophilic substitution. This finding is in agreement with the above orientation mechanism, derived for electrophilic substitutions. On the other hand, electron acceptors such as $COOH$, NO_2, SO_3^-, Cl in the m-position, slow up the decomposition rate. This means that the m-position is negatively charged in relation to the o- and p-positions and hence inhibits nucleophilic substitution. If one attempts to extend these explanatory principles to o- and p-substituted diazonium salts, one encounters considerable inconsistencies which have not as yet been completely explained.

Molecular rearrangements occupy a special position among chemical reactions. It was noted already in the year 1885 by Laar[14] that one and the same substance could be described by several differing structural formulas, depending on experimental conditions, if reactive properties were used as criteria. These separate structures could be interchanged, a phenomenon which was later called tautomerism. Two classes of rearrangements which led to tautomeric products were differentiated: the anionotropic reaction, and the cationotropic or prototropic rearrangement. We know nowadays that this type of reaction is only a special case of general structural rearrangements which are termed nucleophilic or electrophilic, respectively.

In the nucleophilic rearrangements primarily an anion is formed, while the corresponding cation undergoes isomeric structural shifts. In the second category the anion is added at a different position of the cationic molecule. Among the nucleophilic anionotropic rearrangements, there belong, for example, the Wagner-Meerwein rearrangement of isobornylchloride into camphenyl chloride:

---

[13] E. A. Moelwyn-Hughes and P. Johnson, *Trans. Faraday Soc.* **36,** 948 (1940).
[14] C. Laar, *Ber.* **18,** 652 (1885).

the rearrangement of ketoximes into substituted acid amides (Beckmann rearrangement):

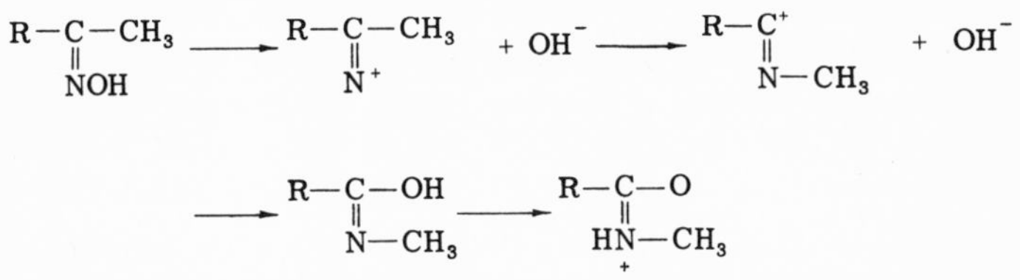

$$R-\underset{\underset{NOH}{\|}}{C}-CH_3 \longrightarrow R-\underset{\underset{N^+}{\|}}{C}-CH_3 + OH^- \longrightarrow R-\underset{\underset{N-CH_3}{\|}}{C^+} + OH^-$$

$$\longrightarrow R-\underset{\underset{N-CH_3}{\|}}{C}-OH \longrightarrow R-\underset{\underset{\overset{HN-CH_3}{+}}{\|}}{C}-O$$

and the rearrangement of phenylhydroxylamine into p-aminophenol:

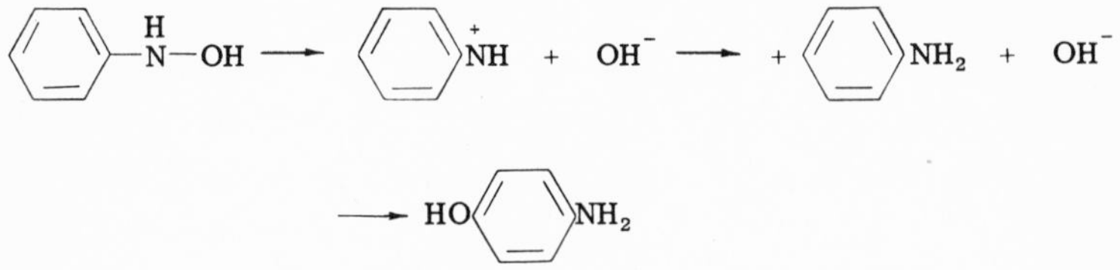

As examples of electrophilic rearrangements one may mention the Claisen reaction, i.e., the rearrangement of an aryl-allyl ether into an o-allylphenol derivative:

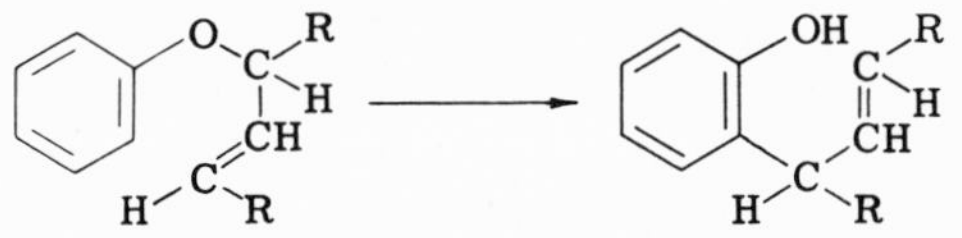

and the benzidine rearrangement, i.e., the change of diphenylhydrazine into p-diaminodiphenyl:

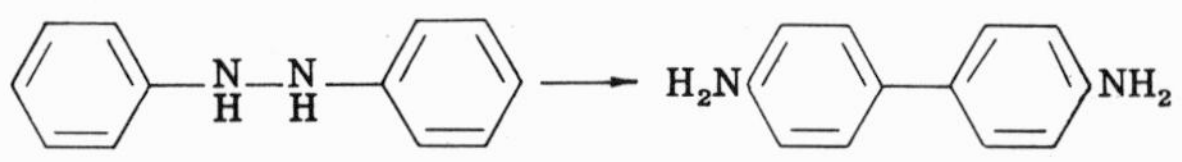

A number of reaction mechanisms have been proposed which take into account that the N—N bond does not rupture, but that the reaction course probably is intramolecular.[15]

[15] P. Jacobson, *Ann.* **428,** 76 (1922); G. W. Wheland and J. R. Schwartz, *J. Chem. Phys.* **17,** 425 (1949); E. D. Hughes and C. K. Ingold, *Quart. Revs. (London)* **6,** 34 (1952). For the base-catalyzed isomerization of olefincarboxylic acids, see A. Lüttringhaus and W. Reif, *Ann.* **618,** 221 (1958).

CHAPTER 22

Nuclear Magnetic Resonance
and Chemical Constitution

We have already encountered nuclear spin of an atomic nucleus in the discussion of the two hydrogen modifications, o- and p-hydrogen (Chapter 18). We saw that different mutual orientation of nuclear spin leads to different selection rules in rotation quantization, so that the heats of the two H_2 modifications differ markedly at low temperatures. The magnetic moment resulting from the spin plays an important role in organic compounds so that the determination of their magnitude by Bloch[1] on the one hand, and Purcell[2] on the other have given a new impetus towards research in this direction.

The magnetic moment of an atomic nucleus is expressed in Bohr magnetons

$$\mu_K = \frac{eh}{4\pi m \cdot c},\tag{83}$$

where 1 nuclear magneton is equal to 5.05×10^{-24} erg/gauss. If an atomic nucleus is introduced into a magnetic field, it is oriented and precesses with a known angular velocity along a plane of a pyramid of known aperture in the direction of the applied magnetic field. The precession frequency, the so-called Larmor frequency ω, is given by:

$$\omega = 2\pi\nu = \frac{2\pi\mu H_0}{\mathbf{I}h}\tag{84}$$

where μ is the magnetic moment, H_0 the magnetic field strength, and $\mathbf{I}$ the spin quantum number of the nucleus. The ratio of magnetic moments

---

[1] F. Bloch, W. W. Hansen, and M. E. Packard, *Phys. Rev.* **69,** 127 (1946).

[2] E. M. Purcell, H. C. Torrey, and R. V. Pound, *Phys. Rev.* **69,** 37 (1946).

to nuclear spin $\gamma = \mu/\mathbf{I}$ is called the magnetogyric ratio. The motion of a spinning top can be created by an induction current in a closed coil, because the number of magnetic field lines which are intercepted by this coil change, owing to the precession motion. Under normal conditions, the current cannot be demonstrated, because many of the rotating atomic nuclei have the same frequency, but precess with different phases along the direction of the field, thereby cancelling the over-all effect. Following Bloch's

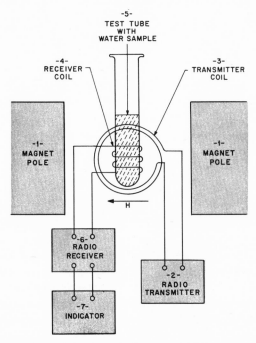

FIG. 37. Simplified schematic diagram of NMR apparatus.

suggestion, an alternating magnetic field H_1 is placed perpendicularly to the outer constant magnetic field H_0. When the same (Larmor) frequency is obtained, the spinning nuclear tops are forced into phase equality. The induction moments of the individual nuclei are added together and thus can be demonstrated. The experimental measurement of the Larmor frequency for individual atomic nuclei, depending on varying μ and I values, is carried out by variation of the applied magnetic field strength H_0, keeping the alternating frequency constant, or by changing the alternating frequency with constant magnetic field. In both cases, a current is induced in a coil, perpendicular to the coil of the alternating field, when the Larmor frequency coincides with the alternating frequency. This case corresponds to resonance which is recorded after suitable amplification. A series of Larmor frequencies result which form the NMR spectrum. The equipment for the production of nuclear magnetic resonance spectra is shown schematically in Fig. 37. The nuclear magnetic moment μ (Fig. 38) precesses

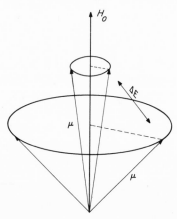

FIG. 38. Precession of the nuclear magnetic momentum along the direction of the magnetic field.

along the direction of the magnetic field H_0 in angles such that a projection of the angular momentum on the direction of H_0 always assumes a whole multiple of $h/2\pi(=\hbar)$. Therefore not all possible precession cones appear, but only certain ones which are discretely different from each other by the magnetic quantum number m_I. It can assume integral or half-integral values.

The corresponding discrete energy states which differ from each other by the amount μH_0 are in thermodynamic equilibrium with the number of occupants, according to a Boltzmann distribution of magnetic nuclear momentum μ, the strength of the magnetic field H_0, and the temperature. Absorption of radiation from the high frequency alternating field H_1, in the case of resonance, produces a transition from one energy level into another whereby the energy difference of two states must be equal. The energy of each magnetic state is given by:

$$E_{m_I} = -\frac{\mu}{\mathbf{I}} H_0 m_{\mathbf{I}}, \tag{85}$$

which is the difference of two energy states, differing in magnetic quantum number:

$$\Delta E = \frac{\mu}{\mathbf{I}} H_0 \Delta m_{\mathbf{I}} = h\nu. \tag{86}$$

According to the selection rules, the change Δm_I must be either $+1$ or -1. One can see that the frequency of the absorbed radiation is equal to the mechanical precession frequency given by Eq. (84) so that ω is $2\pi\nu$. This is the significant difference between nuclear magnetic transition on the one hand and electronic transitions in spectra in the visible and the ultraviolet range on the other. Among the latter, there is no equality between the emitted frequency and angular frequency of the electron, which is only obtained for very small quanta, as shown in the correspondence principle.

The precession frequency shown in Eq. (84) is valid for an idealized, completely isolated, resonant nuclear magnetic moment, without the surrounding electron cloud, or the mutual interaction caused by neighboring moments. However, both circumstances produce changes in the Larmor frequency which are extremely useful in solving problems of chemical constitution. The electrons which spin around the nucleus cause a shielding of the interacting magnetic field. The locally active field strength $H_{eff.}$ at the location of the nuclear spin is smaller by the amount αH_0 than the macroscopic field strength H_0, viz.,

$$H_{eff.} = H_0 - \alpha H_0$$

where α is the diamagnetic shielding constant. It depends on the electron density around the nuclear spin. This diamagnetic shielding causes shifts in the resonance frequency and gives information about the electron density and hence the bond order of the atoms. Depending on the type of the molecule, or the position of the molecule where the nuclear spin is observed, one obtains shifts in resonance frequencies which have been termed chemical

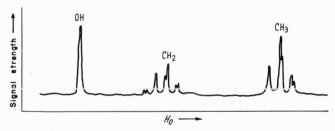

FIG. 39. NMR spectrum of ethanol.

shifts. The NMR spectrum of ethanol is shown in Fig. 39. It consists of three groups of signals which correspond to the three groups CH_3, CH_2, and OH. They are the result of the nuclear magnetic moments of the protons which have been shielded in different degrees by the three groups above, and which appear separated from each other by approximately 40 mgauss. These chemical shifts are field dependent. Their distances can be enlarged by increasing the field strength H_0, since they are proportional to it. The chemical shifts are expressed by the relative shift of the magnetic field strength H_s, over a standard substance H_0, where the resonance signal of the same nucleus is being considered, defined as:

$$\delta \equiv \frac{H_0 - H_s}{H_s}. \tag{87}$$

Water is generally used as a comparison for protons. The value δ has no dimensions and is of the order of magnitude of 10^{-5}. It is larger, the stronger the shielding of the electron cloud, i.e., the larger the electron density surrounding the nuclear spin.

Aside from chemical shifts one observes a splitting of the resonance frequency into a group of signals if one employs high resolution instruments. The strong dispersion in Fig. 39 shows that the CH_3 and CH_2 groups, respectively, consist of three and four separate absorption lines. This splitting is caused by the mutual interaction of the precession frequencies of neighboring nuclear spins. One can describe this action by focusing attention on one nuclear spin and considering the change of the magnetic field H_0 by the neighborhood of a second nuclear spin to a value of H_0'. Depending on whether the nuclear spins are parallel or antiparallel in orientation, one finds an addition or subtraction of the field H_0' to the applied field H_0, so that two new resonance signals appear symmetrically at $H_0 + H_0'$ and at $H_0 - H_0'$. This effect is called spin-spin interaction. It is independent of the field strength and only amounts to a few milligauss.

Only a portion, about one-third, of the elements and their isotopes possess nuclear moments. For example C^{12} has no nuclear moment because neutrons and protons are even and equal and therefore compensate their spins. The same holds for O^{16}. However, nuclear moments are found in the elements frequently encountered in organic compounds:

$$H^1, \quad N^{14}, \quad F^{19}, \quad P^{31}, \quad Cl^{35}, \quad Cl^{37}, \quad C^{13}, \quad Si^{29}$$

Table 30 summarizes a series of the most important isotopes of the elements with their nuclear moments expressed in nuclear magnetons.

The apparatus of the method employed by Purcell is shown schematically in Fig. 37. The conditions for homogeneity and time constancy of the magnetic field are extremely demanding. In order to observe the above-mentioned spin-spin splitting interactions, it must amount to $\frac{1}{10}$ millioersted at a field strength of 10^4 Oe. The use of permanent magnets whose field lines are corrected by weak electric currents in order to obtain parallel positioning has the sole disadvantage that the field strength can-

TABLE 30
Nuclear Magnetic Moments of Some Isotopes

Isotope		Spin $(h/2\pi)$	
H	99.98	1/2	2.79277
D	1.56×10^{-2}	1	0.85741
B^{11}	81.17	3/2	2.689
C^{12}	98.9	0	0
C^{13}	1.1	1/2	0.7023
N^{14}	99.62	1	0.4037
O^{16}	99.757	0	0
F^{19}	100	1/2	2.628
Na^{23}	100	3/2	2.217
Al^{27}	100	5/2	3.641
Si^{28}	92.28	0	0
P^{31}	100	1/2	1.131
S^{32}	95.06	0	0
S^{33}	0.74	3/2	0.6429
Cl^{35}	75.4	3/2	0.8210
K^{39}	93.3	3/2	0.3910
Br^{79}	50.5	3/2	2.106
I^{127}	100	5/2	2.809

not be varied and, thereby, field dependent and field independent effects cannot be differentiated.

The application of the NMR method is indeed manifold. The melting process of the high polymer compounds can be followed by observing the line breadth. The natural breadth ΔE of an emission line, according to the Heisenberg Uncertainty Principle, is related with the lifetime $\Delta\tau$ of the excited state such that

$$\Delta E \cdot \Delta\tau \gtrless h. \tag{32}$$

must hold. This lifetime may vary within a range of 10^{-4} to 2 sec and therefore is much longer than the lifetime of the excited electronic state (10^{-18}

sec). Correspondingly, the above correlation of natural line breadth is smaller by the same amount and often falls below 1 cycle.

The magnetic resonance lines suffer a broadening owing to a series of factors among which the most important is the magnetic dipole-dipole interaction. In the solid state the broadening can amount to several kilocycles. Melting and destruction of the solid spatial relationship of the nuclear magnetic moments to each other eliminates such dipole-dipole interaction. Heat motion permits all possible orientations, so that the interactions on the average cancel out. The latter comes about by the rapid heat agitation of the molecule in contrast to the long duration of the precession mode. This explains why the resonance lines become sharper during the melting process. This phenomenon has been employed in order to determine the degree of order of high polymers at various temperature ranges.[3]

The frequency of chemical exchange can also be obtained from studies of line structure. The splitting of electron-coupled spin-spin interaction is absent if the residence time of the nuclear spin falls below a certain minimum. For example, the phenomena of nuclear magnetic resonance of H_2O/CH_3CH_2OH mixtures can be explained as follows.[4] The δ values of the proton spin in water and OH group of alcohols are 0.34×10^{-5} and 0.42×10^{-5}, respectively, for mixtures containing up to 20% water. For larger ratios one observes only a single line which corresponds to the δ value of 0.355×10^{-5}. The reason for the coincidence of both δ values must be found in the rapid interchange of protons between alcohol and water molecules which presumably takes place along hydrogen bonds.

The so-called electron paramagnetic resonance is based on similar phenomena. A free uncoupled electron is characterized by the magnetic moment

$$\mu = g \sqrt{\tfrac{1}{2}(\tfrac{1}{2} + 1)}\mu_B \qquad (g\text{-factor}, \ \mu_B = \text{Bohr magneton})$$

and spin $S = \tfrac{1}{2}$. Application of an external field H_0 produces a precession motion of the electron spin vector along the axis of the magnetic field H_0. A perpendicular high frequency magnetic field H_1 produces precession of the electrons (Larmor precession) in resonance if both frequencies (the H_1 field and the Larmor precession) coincide. In such a case, there is absorption of energy from the field H_1, which is registered as a signal (Zavorsy, 1945).

---

[3] A. Odajima, J. Sohma, and M. Koike, *J. Chem. Phys.* **23,** 1959 (1955).

[4] I. Weinberg and J. R. Zimmermann, *J. Chem. Phys.* **23,** 748 (1955); cf. also H. S. Gutowsky and A. Saika, *ibid.* **21,** 1688 (1953).

Electron paramagnetic resonance measurements are of considerable importance in the study of electric fields in crystals of paramagnetic salts of the transition elements and the rare earth elements.[5] Free radicals are demonstrated by this method in a highly specific manner. Their spectra are not completely explained at present. The electron paramagnetic resonance of p-semiquinone[6] consists of a signal which is split into five lines (Fig. 40). It has been explained as coupling of a free electron with the

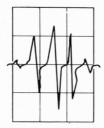

Fig. 40. Electron paramagnetic resonance spectrum of p-semi-quinone.

magnetic moments of the four equivalent protons. There result five possible modes of orientation of the moments to the direction of the magnetic moment of the free electron (hyperfine structure).[7]

[5] D. Bleaney and K. W. H. Stevens, *Repts. Progr. in Phys.* **16,** 108 (1953).

[6] J. E. Wertz and J. L. Vivo, *J. Chem. Phys.* **23,** 2441 (1955).

[7] The organic chemist will find the recent works by L. M. Jackman ("Applications of Nuclear Magnetic Resonance to Organic Chemistry." Pergamon, London, 1959) and J. D. Roberts ("Nuclear Magnetic Resonance, Application to Organic Chemistry." McGraw-Hill, New York, 1959) particularly rewarding. For more rigorous treatment of NMR, see J. A. Pople, W. G. Schneider, and H. J. Bernstein, "High-Resolution Magnetic Resonance." McGraw-Hill, New York, 1959.

Bibliography

[*The following books are recommended for further study.*]

BRAND, J. C. D., and SPEAKMAN, J. C., "Molecular Structure." Edward Arnold, London, 1960.

BRAUDE, E. A., and NACHOD, F. C., "Determination of Organic Compounds by Physical Methods," Vol. I. Academic Press, New York, 1955.

CARTMELL, E., and FOWLES, G. W. A., "Valency and Molecular Structure." Academic Press, New York, 1956.

COTTRELL, T. L., "The Strength of Chemical Bonds." Academic Press, New York, 1954.

COULSON, C. A., "Valence." Oxford Univ. Press (Clarendon), London and New York, 1951.

DAUDEL, R., LEFEBVRE, R., and MOSER, C., "Quantum Chemistry." Interscience, New York, 1959.

DEWAR, M. J. S., "The Electronic Theory of Organic Chemistry." Oxford Univ. Press (Clarendon), London and New York, 1949.

GLASSTONE, S., "Theoretical Chemistry," 2nd ed. Van Nostrand, Princeton, New Jersey, 1945.

HARTMANN, H., "Theorie der chemischen Bindung auf quantentheoretischer Grundlage." Springer, Berlin, 1954.

HARTMANN, H., "Die chemische Bindung." Springer, Berlin, 1955.

HINE, J., "Physical Organic Chemistry." McGraw-Hill, New York, 1956.

HÜCKEL, E., "Grundzüge der Theorie ungesättigter und aromatischer Verbindungen." Verlag Chemie, Berlin, 1938.

KAUZMANN, W., "Quantum Chemistry: An Introduction." Academic Press, New York, 1957.

KLAGES, F., "Lehrbuch der organischen Chemie," de Gruyter, Berlin, 1955.

Nachod, F. C., and Phillips, W. D., "Determination of Organic Structures by Physical Methods," Vol. II. Academic Press, New York, 1962.

PAULING, L., and WILSON, E. B., JR., "Introduction to Quantum Mechanics." McGraw-Hill, New York, 1935.

PULLMAN, B., and PULLMAN, A., "Les Theories Electroniques de la Chimie Organique." Masson, Paris, 1952.

WHEATLEY, P. W., "Determination of Molecular Structure," Oxford Univ. Press (Clarendon), London and New York, 1959.

WHELAND, G. W., "Resonance in Organic Chemistry." Wiley, New York, 1955.

AUTHOR INDEX

Numbers in parentheses are footnote numbers. They are inserted to indicate that the reference to an author's work is cited with a footnote number and his name does not appear on that page.

SUBJECT INDEX

A

Acenes, 146
Acetic acid, 69, 133
Acetoacetic ester, 54
Acetone, 145
Acetonitrile, 86, 87
Acetylene, 85, 136
Acridine, 163
Activated complex, 172
β-Alanine, 107
Albumin, 107
Alkali halides, lattice energies, 46
Alkyl halides, dipole moments, 101
Amino acids, 107
p-Aminobenzoic acid, 138
Aminobenzoic acids, 100
Aminocaproic acid, 107
p-Aminophenol, 185
p,p'-Aminostilbene, 88
Ammonia, 166, 178
Aniline, 69, 135, 170, 180
Anionoid reactions, 166
Anionotropic reaction, 184
Anisole, 113
Anthracene, 60, 64, 69, 121, 122, 146, 169, 170
Antibonding states, 151, 152
Aromaticity, 70
Aryl halides, dipole moments, 101
Atomic distance, 85
Atomic refractions, 110
Atomic susceptibilities, 119
Auxochromic group, 141
Azulene, 69, 148

B

Balmer series, 10
Bathychromic effect, 143, 144, 146
Beckmann rearrangement, 185
Benzaldehyde, 153
Benzene, 55, 60, 64, 68, 69, 70, 72, 73, 85, 87, 89, 90, 121, 122, 146, 147, 179, 180, 181
  MO calculation, 62

resonance energy, 59
Benzoic acid, 69, 70, 134, 138
Benzofulvene, 150, 152
Benzophenone, 153
Benzophenone potassium, 126
Benzoquinone, 69
Beryllium compounds, 81
4R-Bicyclo-(2,2,2)-octane-1-oic acid, 139
Biphenyl, 60, 64, 69, 72, 73, 89, 122, 144, 146
Black body, 3
Bohr atomic model, 9, 29
Bohr magneton, 123, 124, 125, 190, 192
Boltzmann constant, 2
Boltzmann distribution, 188
π-Bond, MO, 80
Bond order, 85, 86
Bond strength, 44
Bonding states, 151, 152
Boron compounds, 81
Bromoacetylene, 102
Bromobenzene, 182
1-Bromo-2-chloroethane, 177
1-Bromo-2,4-dinitrobenzene, 183
Bromoethylene, 102
Butadiene, 60, 64, 68, 69, 89, 151, 169
sec. Butanol, 173
Butene, 68
Butyric acid, 134

C

Camphenyl chloride, 184
Camphor, 177
Canonical structures, 67, 147, 148, 150
Carbanion, 178
Carbazole, 135
Carbonium ion, 177
Catalysis, 165
Charge distribution, 167, 170
Chelates, 52
Chemical bond, 43, 109
Chemical shift, 190
Chlorobenzene, 88, 99, 105, 176, 182
Chloroethylene, 136

199